Contents

UNIT 1 Alphabet, Consonants S, T, B, H, M, K, J, F, G

Theme: Fun at Home

UNIT 2 Consonants L, D, N, W, C, R, P, Q, V, X, Y, Z

Theme: Eyes on Animals

Consonants l, d, n

Consonants w, c, r

UNIT 3

Short Vowels

Theme: Under, Over, and All Around

Short Vowels u, o, e

UNIT 4

Introduction to Long Vowels

Theme: Fun in the Sun

Long Vowels a, i, u, o, e

Read Aloud

Clap Your Hands

compiled by Marc Brown

Clap your hands, clap your hands,
Clap them just like me.
Touch your shoulders,
Touch your shoulders,
Touch them just like me.
Tap your knees, tap your knees,
Tap them just like me.
Shake your head, shake your head,
Shake it just like me.
Clap your hands, clap your hands.
Now let them quiet be.

TALK About It
What do you like to do to have fun?

Dear Family,

In this unit, "Fun At Home," your child will learn the sounds the letters **s**, **t**, **b**, **h**, **m**, **k**, **j**, **f**, and **g** make at the beginning of words. As your child develops an understanding of these sounds, you may wish to try these activities.

- Help your child identify the letters that begin the names of familiar things around the house. Look for things that begin with the sounds of **s**, **t**, **b**, **h**, **m**, **k**, **j**, **f**, and **g**. Also think of words that rhyme with objects you find at home such as sink-wink, table-able, bed-red, hat-cat, mug-jug, key-me, jar-car, fan-pan, and game-same.
- You and your child will enjoy reading these books together. Look for them in your local library.

The House Book
by Keith Duquette

No Jumping on the Bed!
by Tedd Arnold

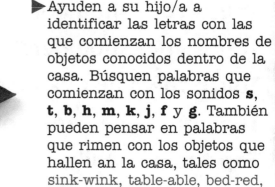

Sincerely,

____

hat

cat

Estimada familia,

En esta unidad titulada "Diversión en el hogar," (Fun At Home) su hijo/a estudiará los sonidos que las letras **s**, **t**, **b**, **h**, **m**, **k**, **j**, **f** y **g** hacen al principio de las palabras. A medida que su hijo/a aprenda estos sonidos, quizás deseen hacer las siguientes actividades.

- Ayuden a su hijo/a a identificar las letras con las que comienzan los nombres de objetos conocidos dentro de la casa. Búsquen palabras que comienzan con los sonidos **s**, **t**, **b**, **h**, **m**, **k**, **j**, **f** y **g**. También pueden pensar en palabras que rimen con los objetos que hallen an la casa, tales como sink-wink, table-able, bed-red, hat-cat, mug-jug, key-me, jar-car, fan-pan y game-same.
- Ustedes y su hijo/a disfrutarán leyendo estos libros juntos. Búsquenlos en su biblioteca local.

The House Book
de Keith Duquette

No Jumping on the Bed!
de Tedd Arnold

Sinceramente,

____

Name ________________________________

My Letter Book

Aa 

Bb 

Cc 

Directions: Help children identify and name the pictures.

Dd

Ee

Ff

Gg

Hh

Ii

Jj

Kk

HOME With your child, say words that begin with the same sound as the picture names on this page, such as *gate-goat*.

Directions: Say the name of each picture. Then have children repeat the name.

Name ______________________________

Ll

Mm

Nn

Oo

Pp

Qq

Rr

Ss

Directions: Ask children to name the pictures they recognize. Then have them say the name of each picture with you.

Tt 

Uu 

Vv 

Ww 

Xx 

Yy 

Zz 

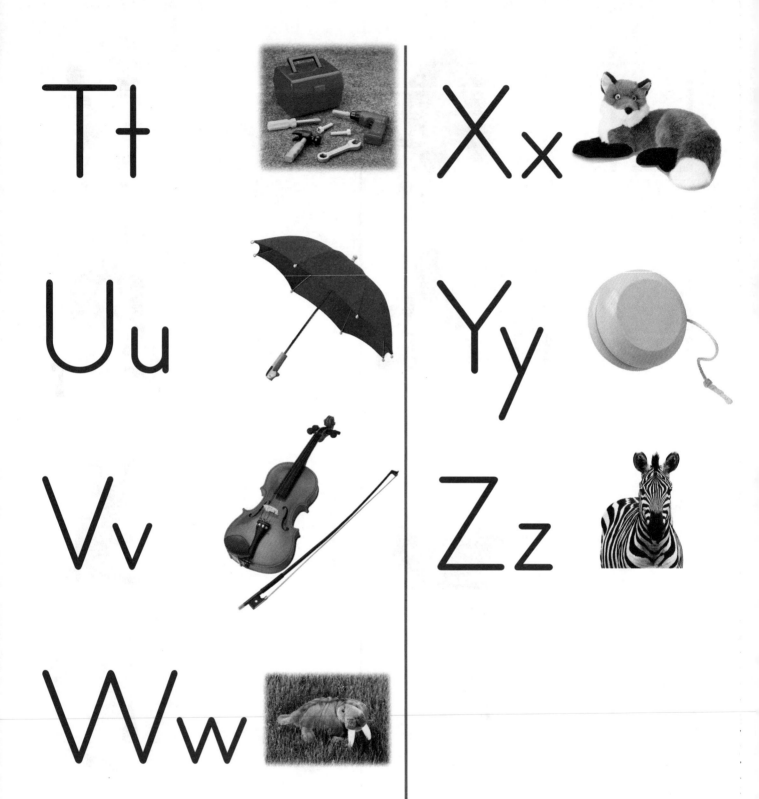

Directions: Say the name of each picture. Then, have children repeat the name.

HOME Look in a magazine with your child to point out and name the letters of the alphabet.

Name ________________________________

Tt

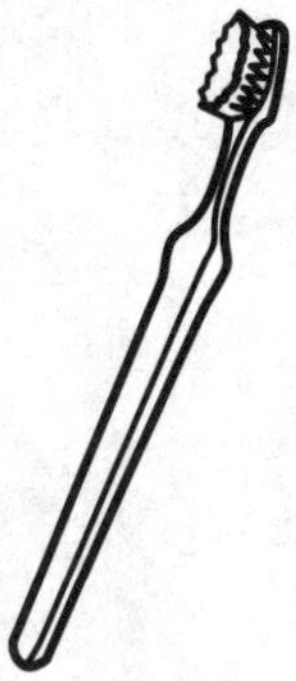

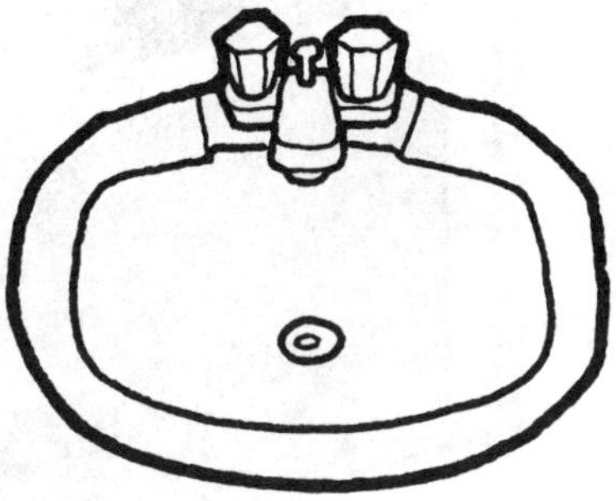

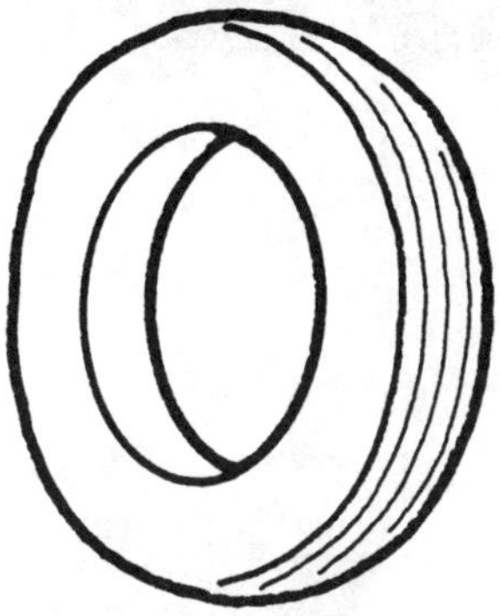

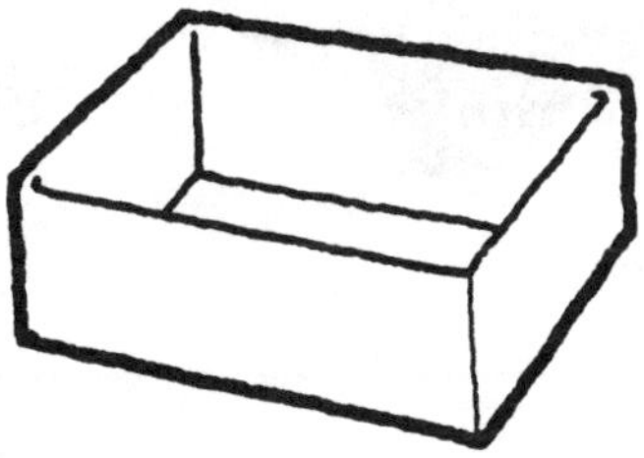

Directions: Help children identify the pictures. If a picture name begins with the sound of *t*, have children color the picture.

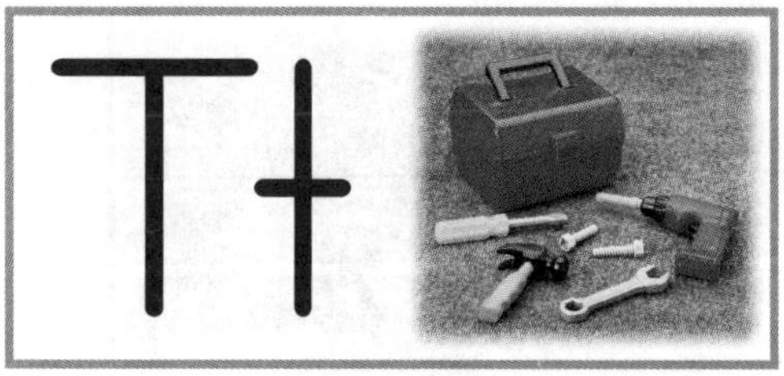

Directions: Ask children to identify the beginning sound of *toy*, then circle each toy that begins with the *t* sound. Children may practice writing *t* on the line.

HOME Ask your child to name toys that he or she has that begin with the *t* sound.

Name ______________________________

Tt

Directions: Help children name the pictures. If a picture name begins with the sound of *t*, have children print *Tt* on the line.

Tt

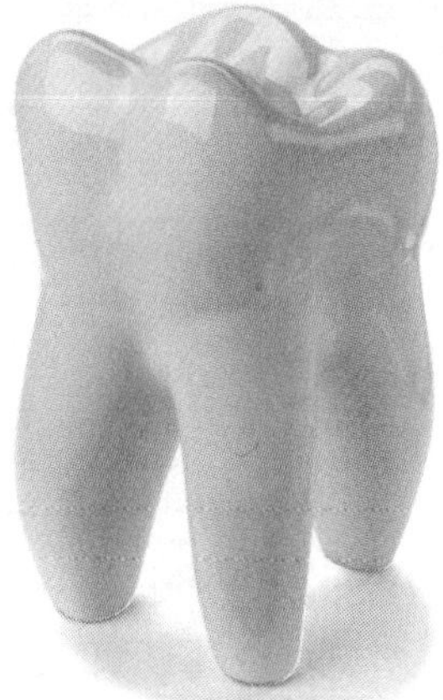

ooth

tape

ub

iger

Directions: Have children name each picture and write the letter *t* to complete each word. Point to and say each word as children say it with you.

HOME Help your child make up silly phrases using words that begin with *t*, such as *two turtles in a tub*.

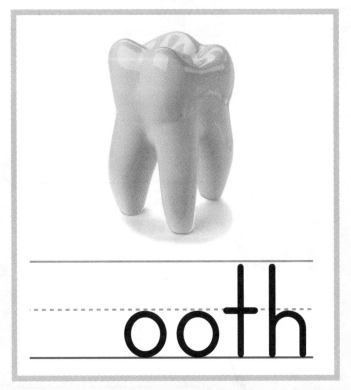

Name ______________________________

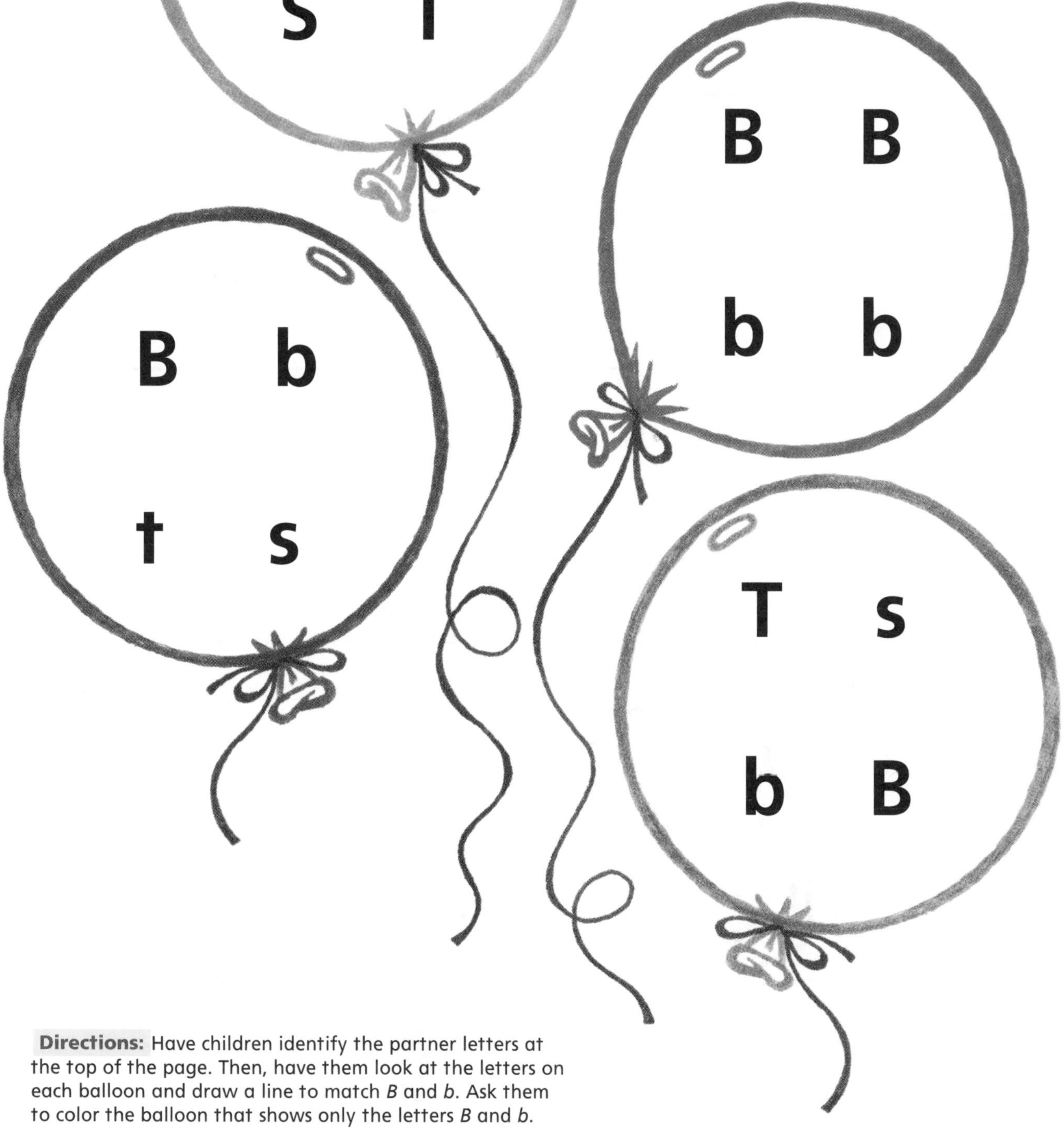

Directions: Have children identify the partner letters at the top of the page. Then, have them look at the letters on each balloon and draw a line to match *B* and *b*. Ask them to color the balloon that shows only the letters *B* and *b*.

BB

bb

Bb

bib

Directions: Have children trace the letters and write their own *B* and *b* on the lines. Then, have them identify the picture and trace *b* to complete the word.

HOME Have your child print *B* and *b*. Write the words *bye, bye baby*. Have your child count the *b's* in the words and trace over them.

Name ______________________________

Bb

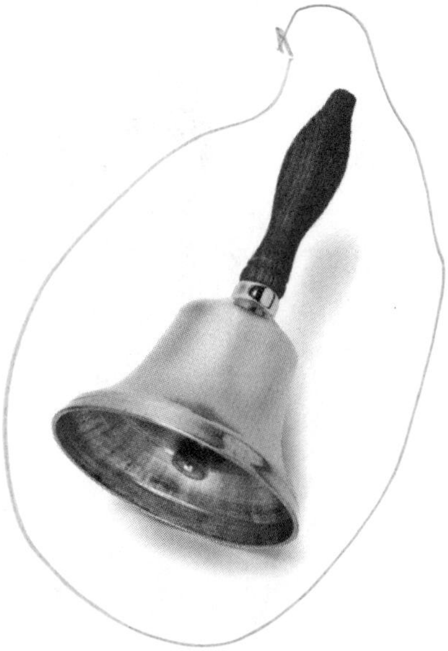

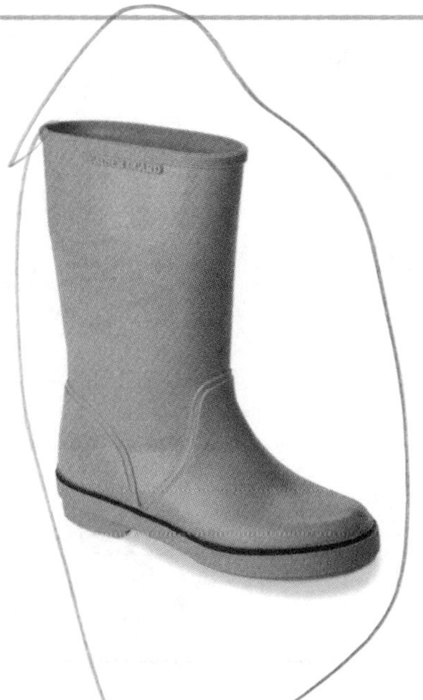
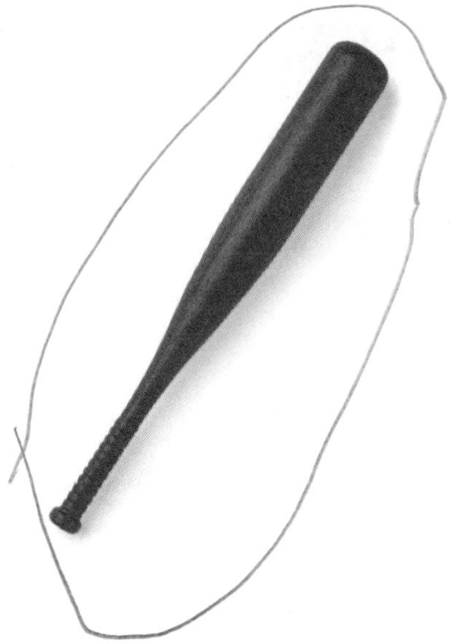

Directions: Help children identify the pictures. If a picture name begins with the sound of *b*, have children circle the picture.

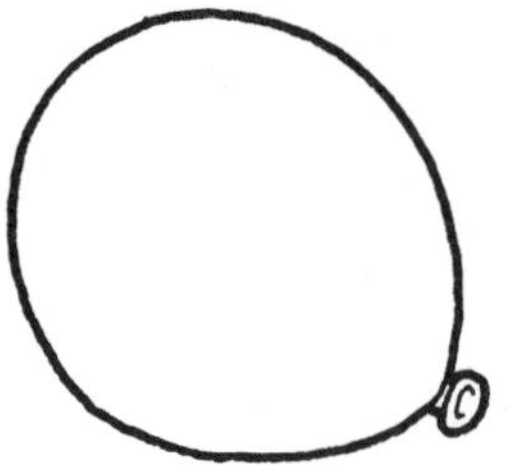

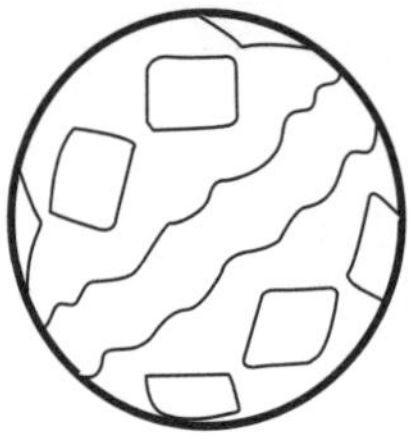

b b

Directions: Ask children to identify the beginning sound of *box*. Have them color each thing that begins with the sound of *b*, and draw a line from the item to the gift box. They can practice writing *b* on the line.

HOME Have your child write several *Bb*s on a paper bag. Help your child find items to put into the bag whose names begin with the sound of *b*.

Name ______________________________

Bb

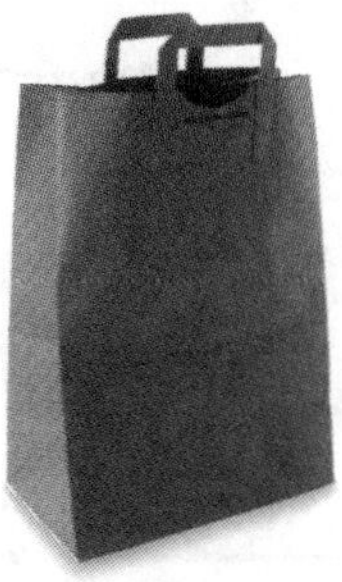

Directions: Help children name the pictures. If a picture name begins with the sound of *b*, have children print *Bb* on the line.

Bb

ball

ird

ee

ook

Directions: Have children name each picture and write the letter *b* to complete each word. Point to and say each word as children say it with you.

HOME

Write the animal names *bat*, *bee*, *bird*, *bunny*, and *bug*, without the *b*. Have your child write *b* to complete the words and draw pictures.

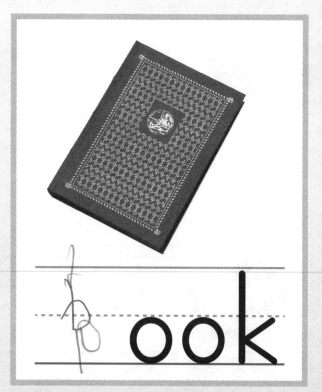

Name ______________________________

 t B s S	 T B s b
 b S t T	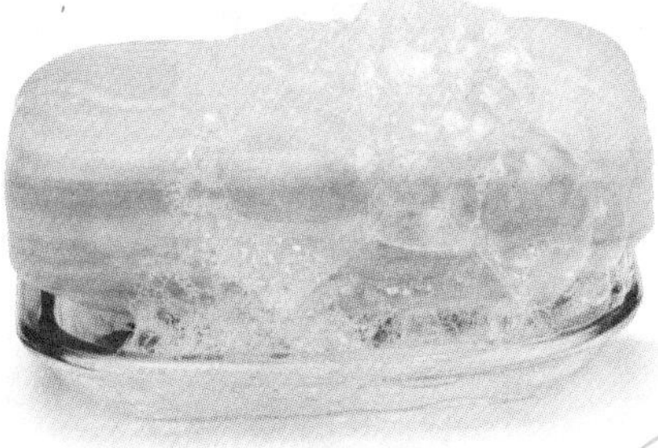 t S B s
 T b s B	 T s b t

Directions: Have children draw a line to match the letter under the picture to its partner letter.

Ss

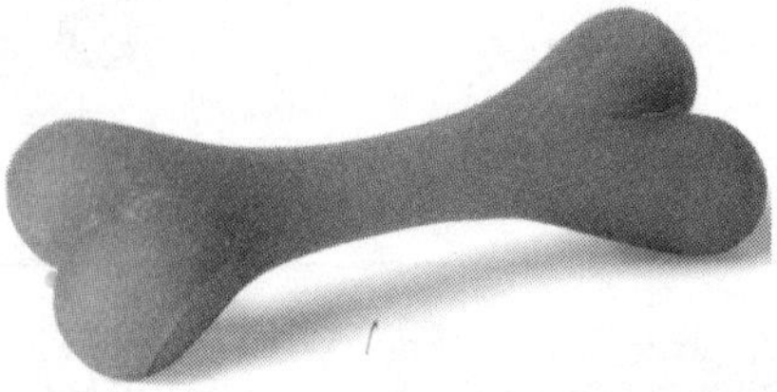

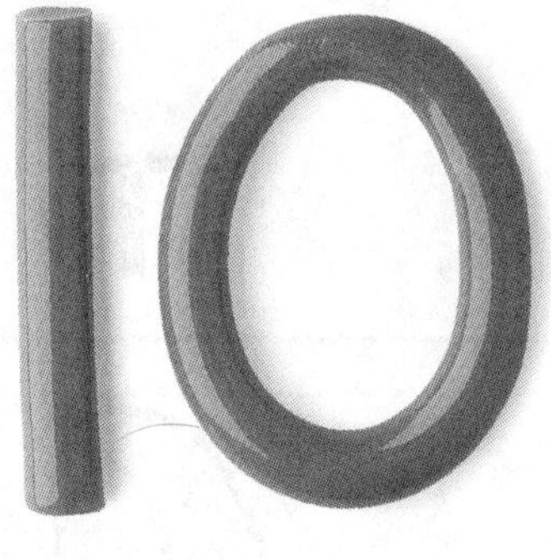

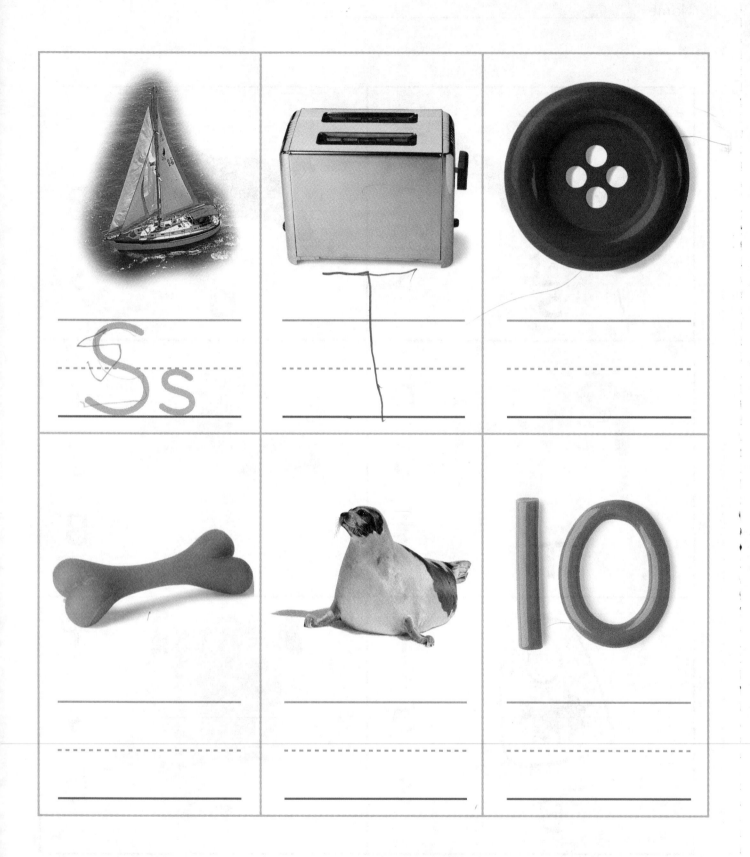

Directions: Have children name each picture, and then trace or write the partner letters that stand for its beginning sound.

HOME Have your child name the pairs of pictures that begin with the same sound and then think of other objects that begin with *s*, *t*, and *b*.

Name ______________________________

is on
my the

My  is on the  .

My  is on the  .

My  is on the  .

My  is on the 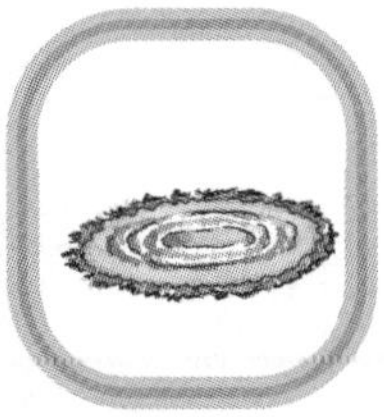 .

Directions: Read the words in the box and have children repeat them. Invite children to say and trace the word in each sentence. Then, read the sentences with children.

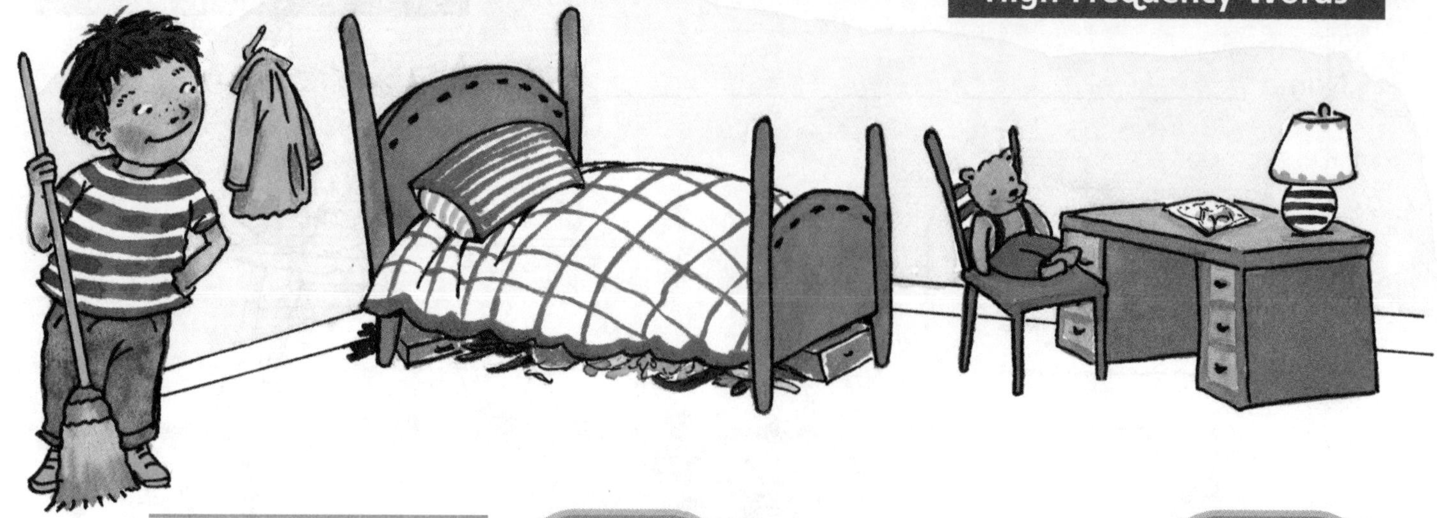

■ My  is on the .

● My  is on the .

▲ My 

is on the .

★ My  is on the 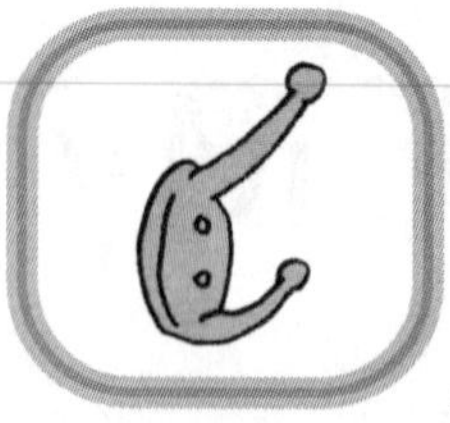.

Directions: Help children to read each sentence. Then, have them trace each word to complete the sentence. Invite them to read the sentences again.

HOME Have your child read each story to you. Help your child use pictures and words to write the sentence: *My ____is on the ____.*

Name ____________

Moving Day

1 My bed is on the van.

FOLD

4 The van is on the way.

Directions: Read the story aloud, and discuss the pictures with children.

2

My box is on the van.

My bike is on the van.

3

FOLD

Name ______________________________

Directions: Have children identify the partner letters at the top of the page. Then, have children follow the alternating letters *H* and *h* and draw a line to get the hippo back to her house.

Hh

H H

h h

H h

hat

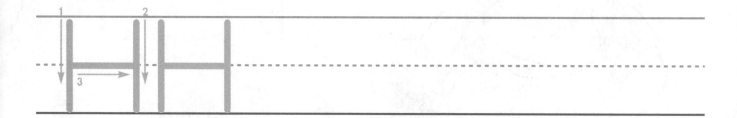

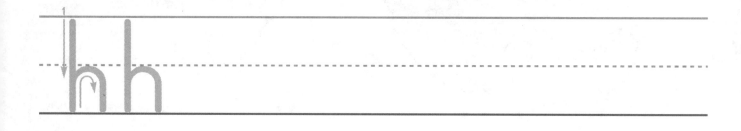

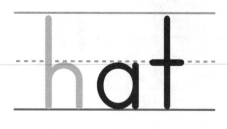

Directions: Have children trace the letters and write their own *H* and *h* on the lines. Then, have them identify the picture and complete the word.

HOME Have your child print *H* and *h*. Write the words *happy home*, omitting the *h*'s. Have your child complete the words.

Name ______________________________

Hh 

		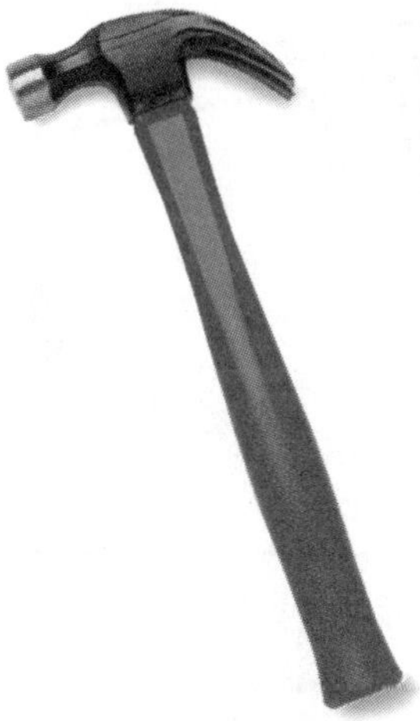

Directions: Help children identify the pictures. If a picture name begins with the sound of *h*, have children circle the picture.

Hh

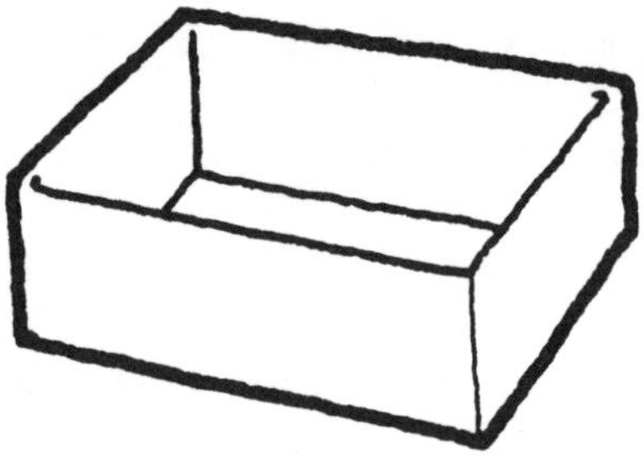

h h

Directions: Ask children to identify the beginning sound of *horse*. Then, have them color each item that begins with the *h* sound. Invite them to practice writing *h* on the line.

HOME Ask your child "*h*-word" questions such as: What *h* word can you ride? (*horse*) Have your child write *h* as the answer is given.

Name ______________________________

Hh 

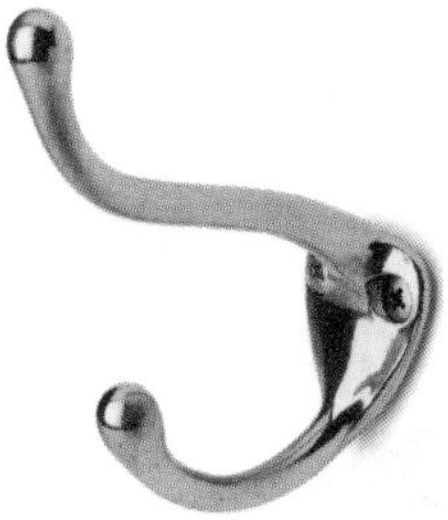

Directions: Help children name the pictures. If a picture name begins with the sound of *h*, have children print *Hh* on the line.

Hh

ive

hat

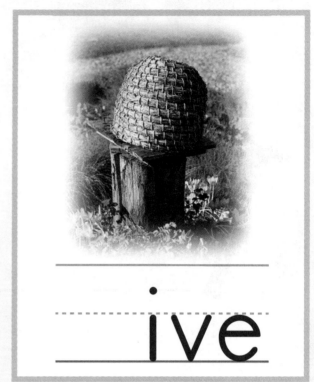

eart

ose

Directions: Have children name each picture and write the letter *h* to complete each word. Point to and say each word as children say it with you.

HOME

Write the words *hat*, *house*, and *hand*, omitting the *h*. Have your child complete the words and draw a picture to show each word.

Name ____________________

Mm

■ m	M	S	H
● M	b	m	s
▲ M	t	h	m
★ m	B	T	M

Directions: Have children identify the letter at the beginning of each row. Ask them to circle the letter in each row that is the partner letter.

1 2 MM

1 mm

Mm

milk

Directions: Have children trace the letters and write their own *M* and *m* on the lines. Then, have them identify the picture and trace the *m* to complete the word.

HOME Invite your child to print *M* and *m*. Then write the word *mouse*, omitting the *m*. Have your child complete the word.

Name ______________________________

Mm

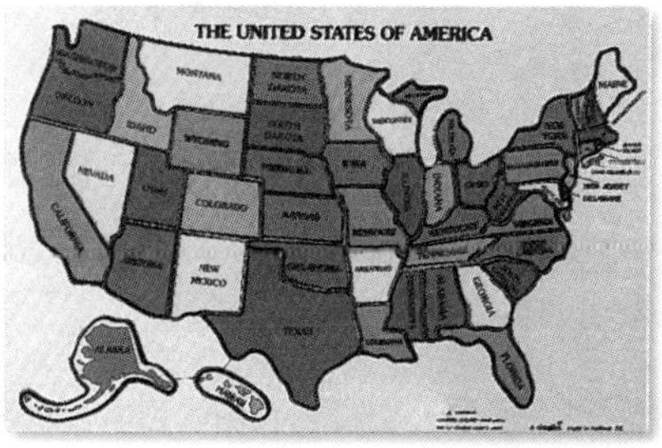

Directions: Help children identify the pictures. If a picture name begins with the sound of *m*, have children circle the picture.

Mm

m m

Directions: Have children circle each food that begins with the sound of *m* and draw a line to the plate. Encourage them to practice printing *m* on the line.

HOME Have your child print *M* on pieces of paper, then place them on things whose names begin with *m*, such as a mug.

Name ______________________________

Mm

Directions: Help children name the pictures. If a picture name begins with the sound of *m*, have children print *M* and *m* on the line.

Mm

ilk

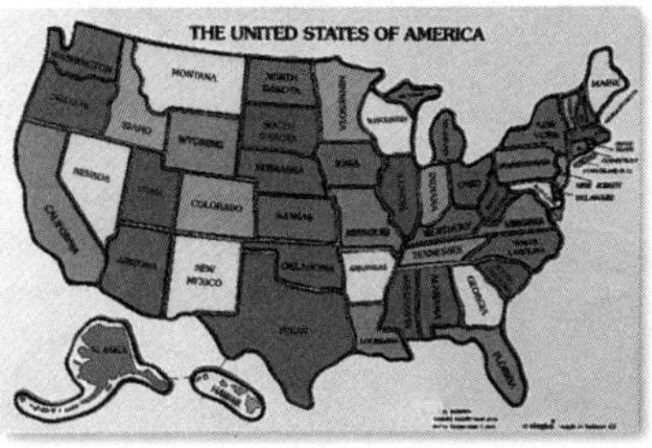

map

en

op

Directions: Have children name each picture and write the letter *m* to complete each word. Point to and say each word as children say it with you.

HOME

Help your child make up sentences using words that begin with the *m* sound, such as *Matt makes maps.*

Name ______________________

Kk

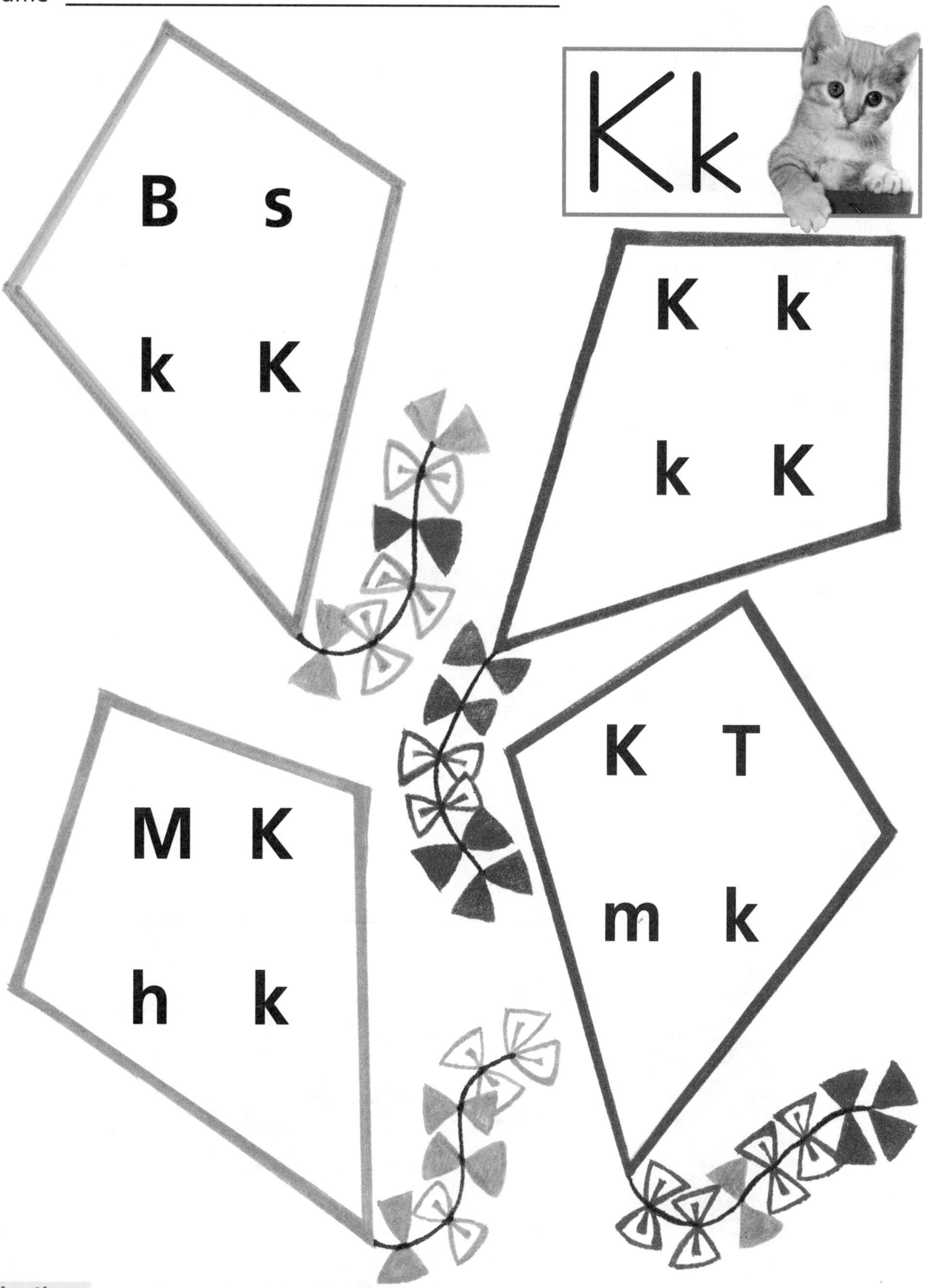

Directions: Have children identify the partner letters at the top of the page. Then have them look at each kite and draw a line to match *K* and *k*. Ask them to color the kite that shows only the letters *K* and *k*.

K K

k k

K k

kitten

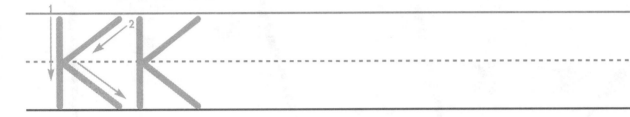

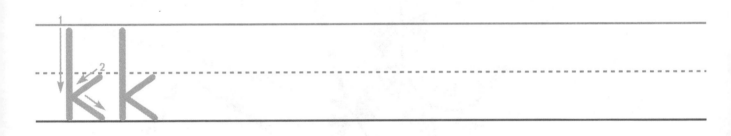

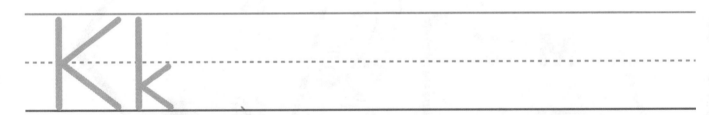

Directions: Have children trace the letters and write their own *K* and *k* on the lines. Then, have them identify the picture and complete the word.

HOME Have your child print *K* and *k*. Write the sentence *The king likes kites*, omitting the *Kk*'s. Have your child write *k* to complete the words.

Name ______________________________

Kk

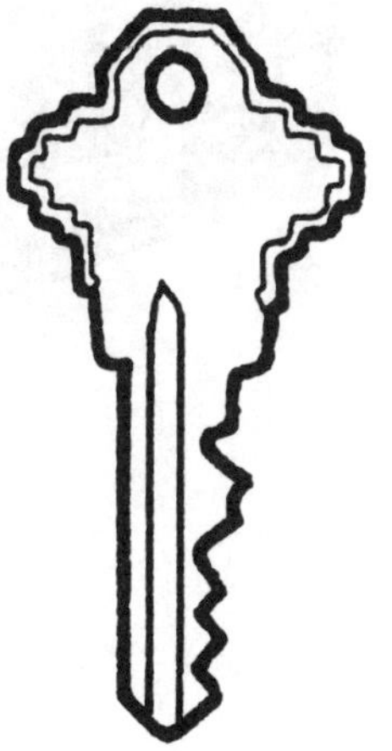

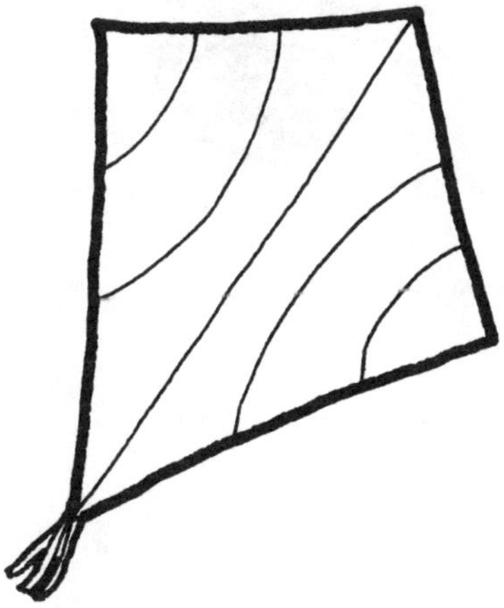

Directions: Help children identify the pictures. If a picture name begins with the sound of *k*, have children color the picture.

Kk

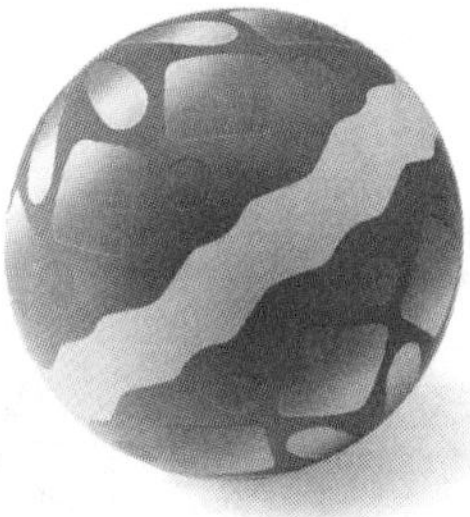

k k

Directions: Ask children to identify the beginning sound of *king*. Then, have them circle each picture whose name begins with the sound of *k*. Invite them to practice writing *k* on the line.

HOME Help your child make up sentences about the picture using words that begin with the *k* sound, such as *King Ken keeps kites.*

Name ______________________

Kk

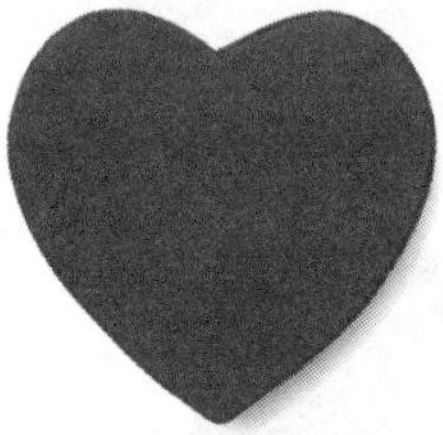

Directions: Help children name the pictures. If a picture name begins with the sound of *k*, have children print *Kk* on the line.

Kk

key

ing

etchup

ite

Directions: Have children name each picture and write the letter *k* to complete each word. Point to and say each word as children say it with you.

HOME Help your child make up sentences using words from the Picture Dictionary, such as *The king spilled ketchup on his kite.*

Name ______________________________

K
m
h
M

H
m
K
k

h
k
M
K

m
k
H
h

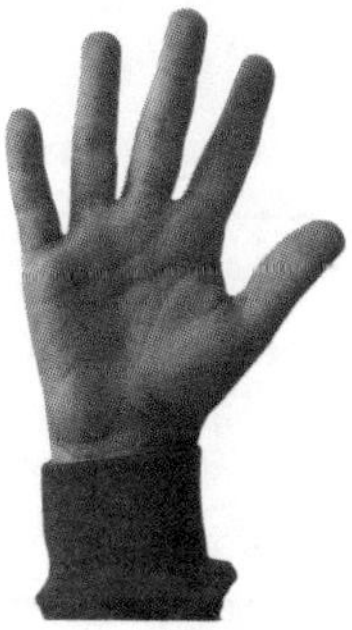

K
h
m
H

M
H
K
m

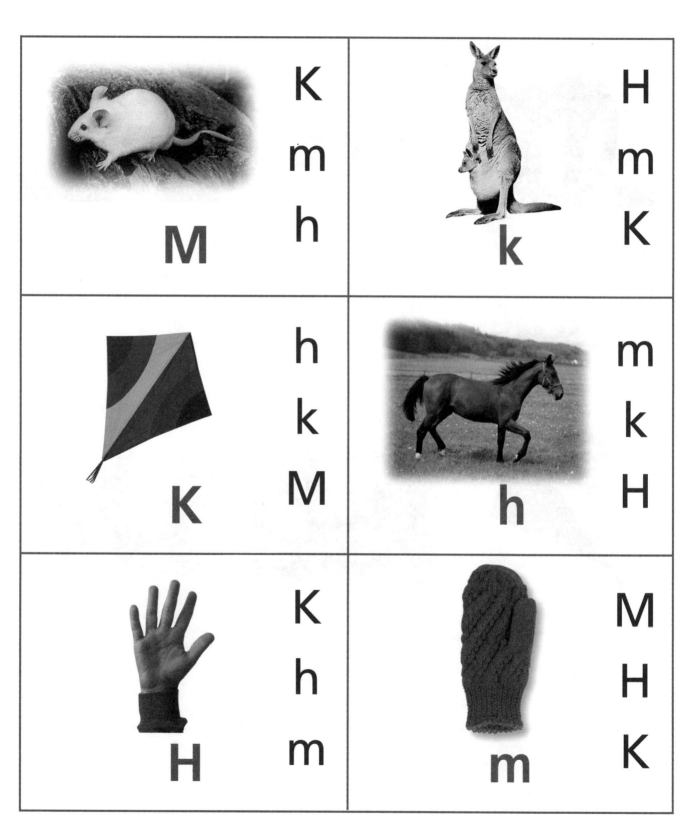

Directions: Have children draw a line to match the letter under the picture to its partner letter.

Mm

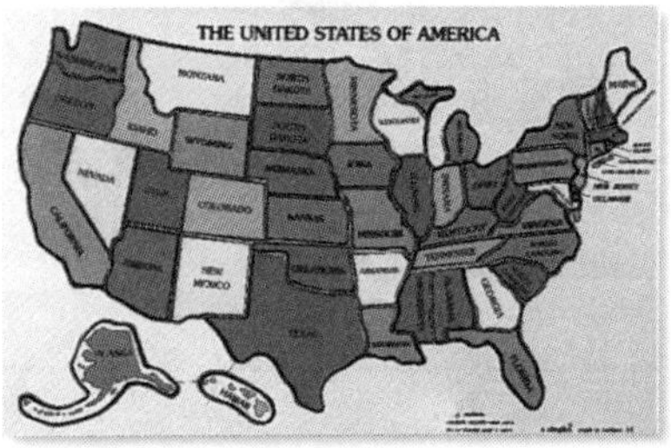

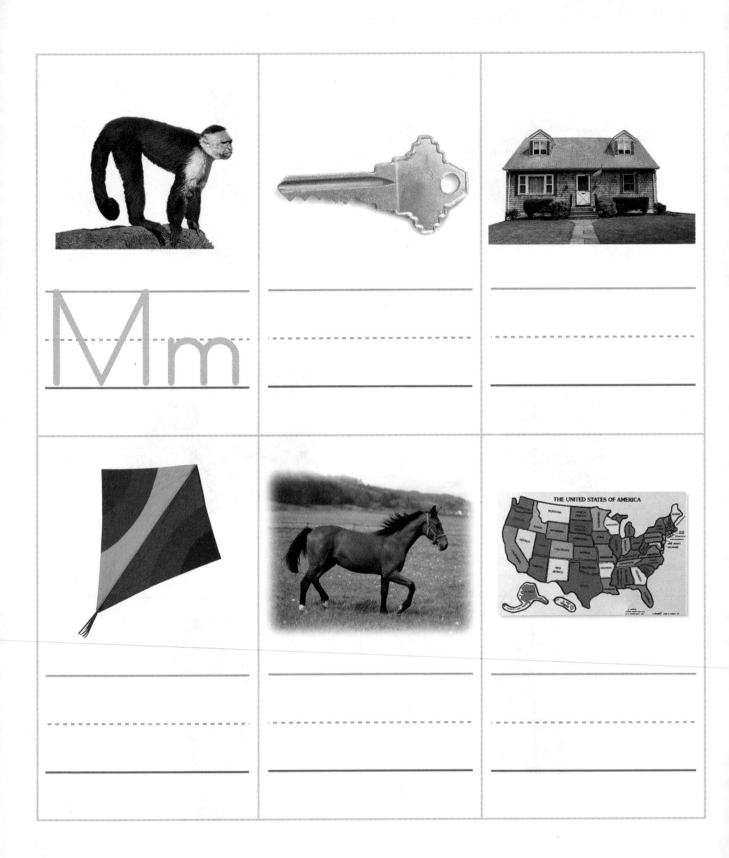

Directions: Have children name each picture, and then trace or write the partner letters that stand for the beginning sounds.

HOME Have your child name the pictures, and then think of other objects that begin with *h*, *m*, or *k*.

Name ______________________________

A for
me not

■ A  is not for me.

● A  is not for me.

▲ A  is not for me.

★ A  is for me.

Directions: Read the words in the box and have children repeat them. Invite children to say and trace the word in each sentence. Then, read the sentences with children.

A for
me not

■ A  is not for me.

● A  is not for me.

▲ A  is not for me.

★ A  is for me.

Directions: Help children to read each sentence. Then, have them trace each word to complete the sentences. Invite them to read the sentences again.

HOME Write the words from this lesson on a sheet of paper. Have your child copy and say the words.

Name ______________

What Is For Me?

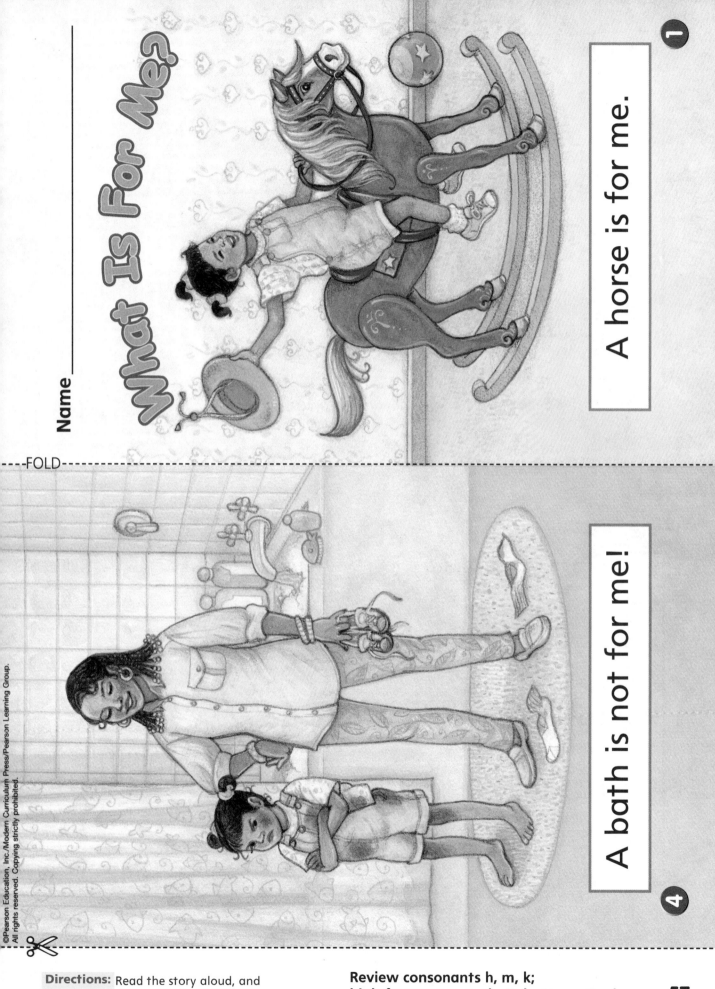

A horse is for me.

1

--FOLD--

A bath is not for me!

4

Directions: Read the story aloud, and discuss the pictures with the children.

A kite is for me.

2

FOLD

The mud is for me.

3

Name ______________________________

Jj

■ j	S	J	T
● J	j	m	t
▲ j	K	M	J
★ J	t	j	s

Directions: Have children identify the letter at the beginning of each row. Ask them to circle the letter in each row that is the partner letter.

J j

J J

j j

J j

jar

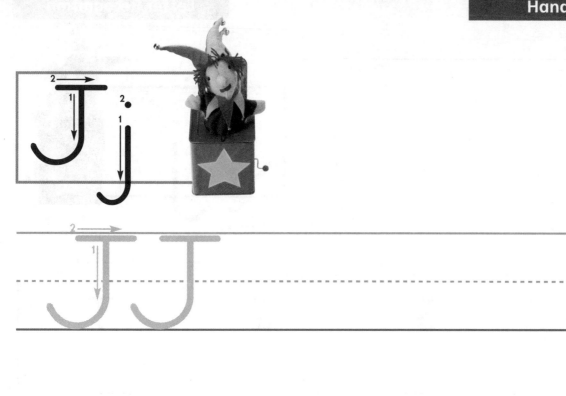

Directions: Have children trace the letters and write their own *J* and *j* on the lines. Then, have them identify the picture and complete the word.

HOME Write the words *jump*, *jiggle*, and *juggle*, omitting the *j*. Have your child complete the words and do the actions.

Name ________________________________

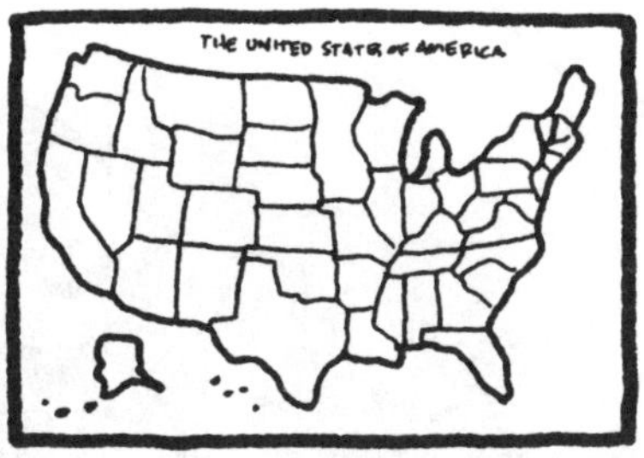

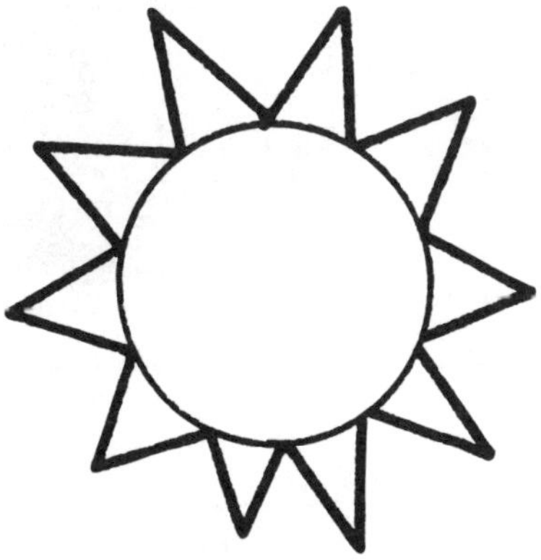

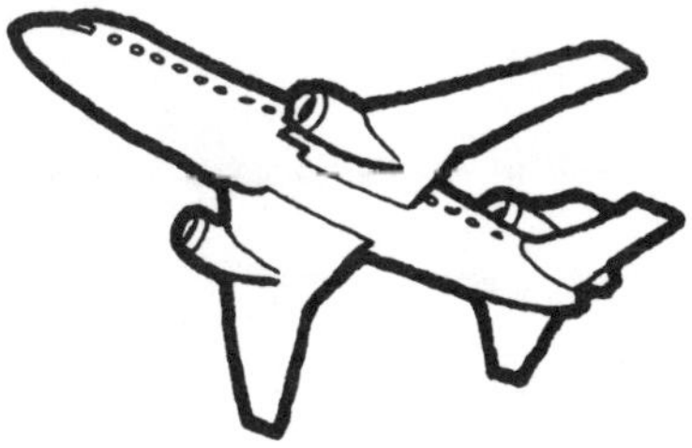

Directions: Help children identify the pictures. If a picture name begins with the sound of *j*, have children color the picture.

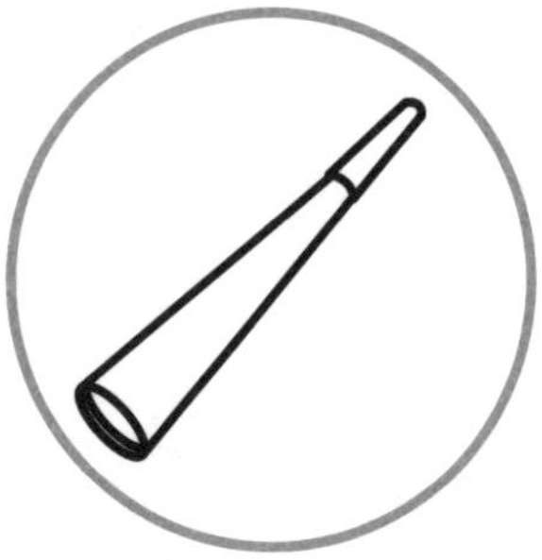

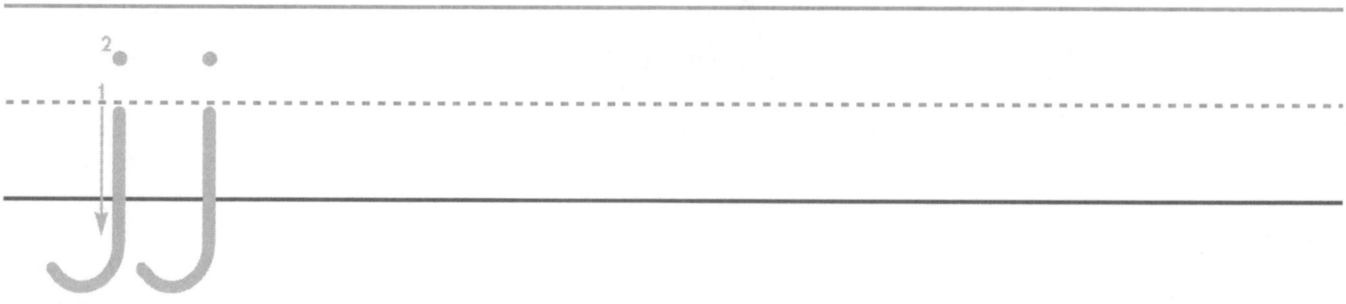

Directions: Ask children to identify the beginning sound of *juggle.* Have children identify each ball showing an object that begins with *j*, and color the ball. Encourage them to practice writing *j* on the line.

HOME Have your children print *J* on pieces of paper and place them on things whose names begin with *j*, such as a *jar* and a *jacket*.

Name ______________________________

Jj

Directions: Help children name the pictures. If a picture name begins with the sound of *j*, have children print *Jj* on the line.

Jj

jacket

ar

et

ump

Directions: Have children name each picture and write the letter *j* to complete each word. Point to and say each word as children say it with you.

HOME Ask your child to draw a picture and tell a story about jumping.

Name ____________________________________

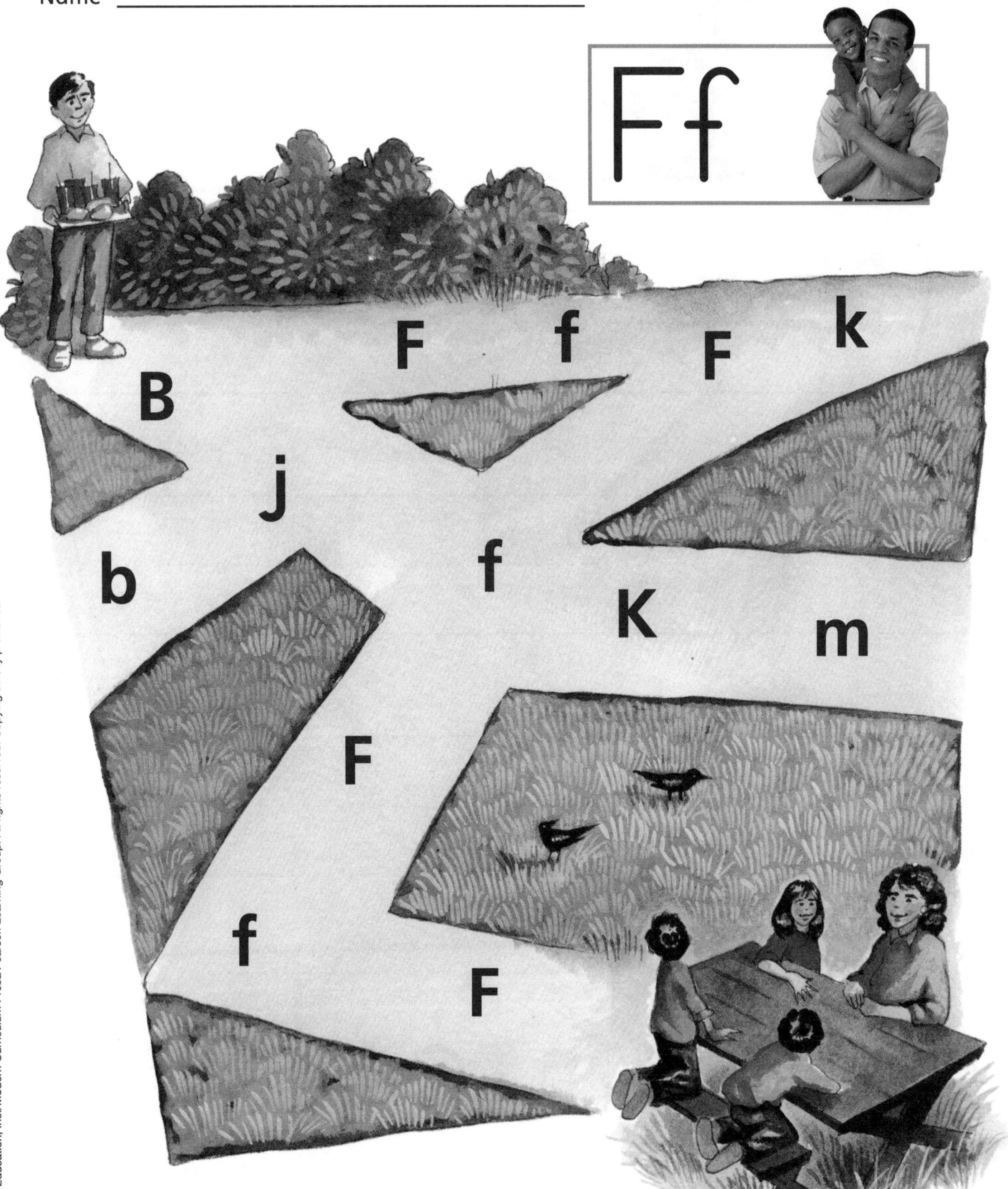

Directions: Have children identify the partner letters at the top of the page. Then have children follow the alternating letters *F* and *f* and draw a line to show how the father gets food to his family.

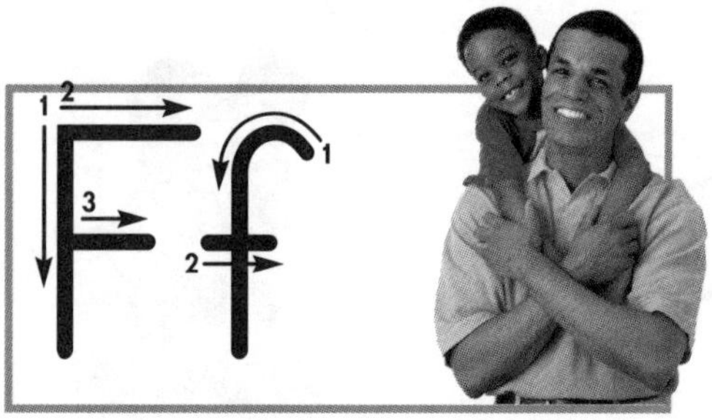

F F

f f

F f

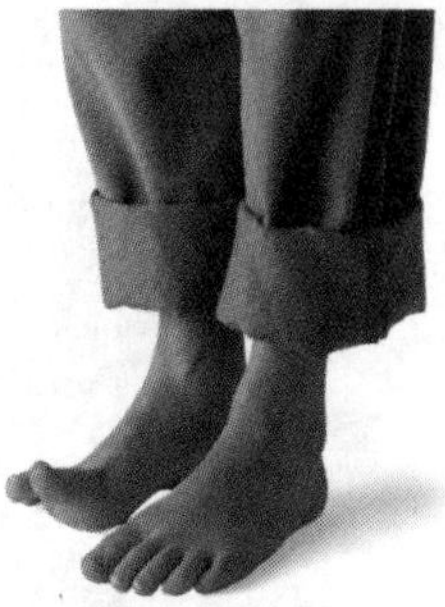

feet

Directions: Have children trace the letters and write their own *F* and *f* on the lines. Then, have them identify the picture and complete the word.

HOME Have your children print *F* and *f*. Write the word *family*, omitting the *f*. Have your child complete the word and draw a picture of your family.

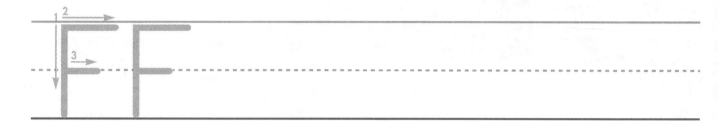

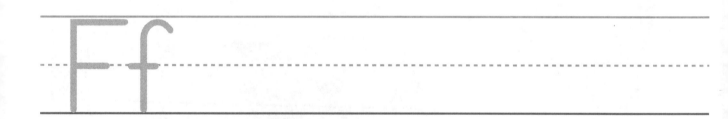

Name ________________________________

Ff

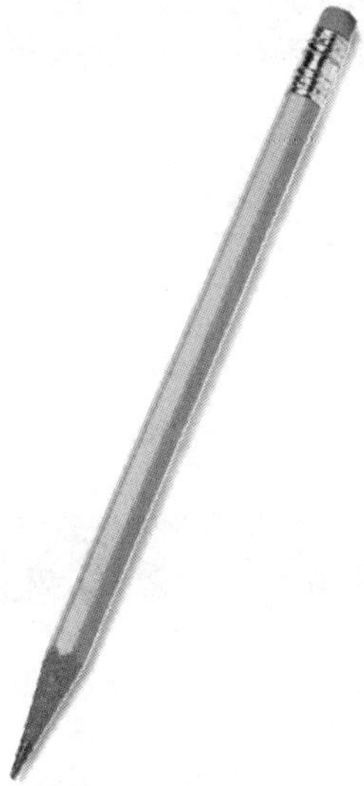

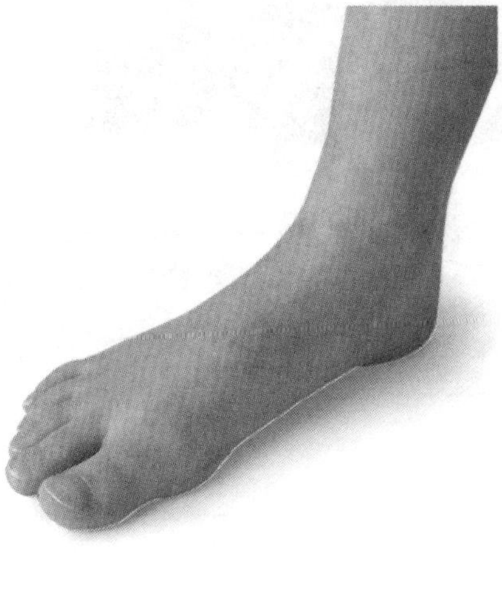

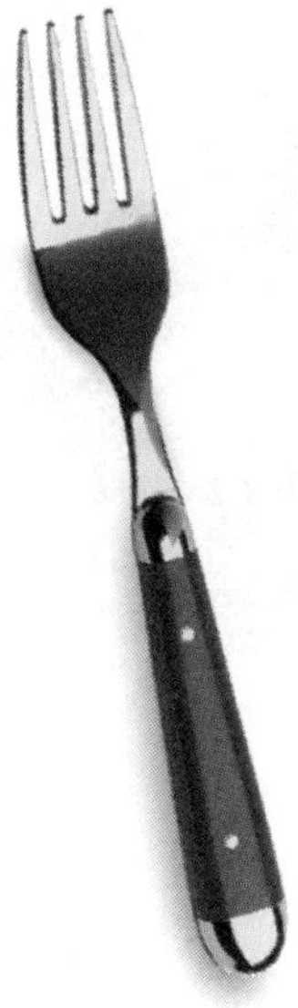

Directions: Help children identify the pictures. If a picture name begins with the sound of *f*, have children circle the picture.

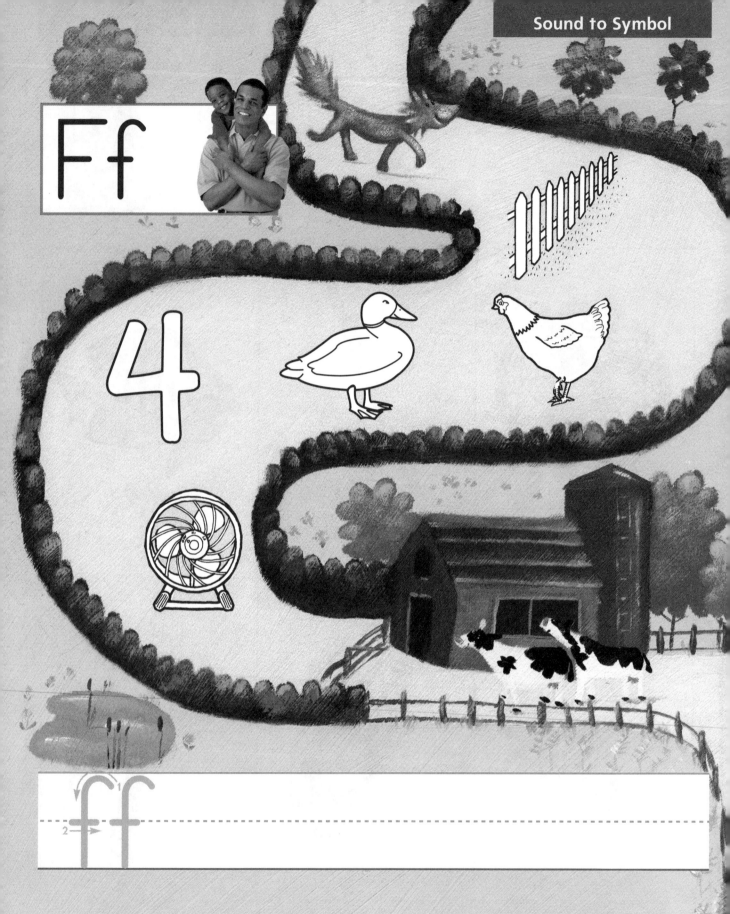

Directions: Ask children to identify the beginning sound of *fox*. Help them name the pictures along the path from the fox to the farm and color each item that begins with *f*. Then, invite them to practice writing *f* on the line.

HOME

Print *Fox is on a farm*. Have your child find the letter *F* or *f* in *Fox* and *farm*. Work together to make up a story about Fox on a farm.

Name ______________________

Ff

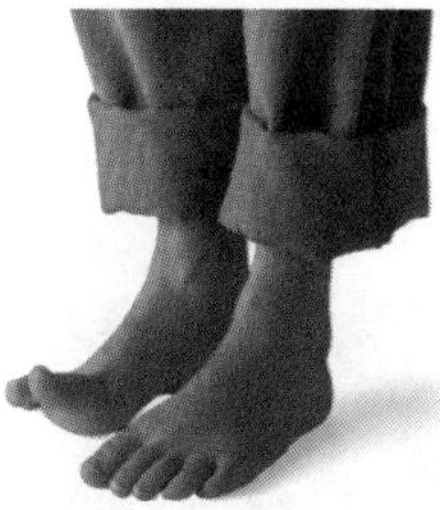

Directions: Help children name the pictures. If a picture name begins with the sound of *f*, have children print *Ff* on the line.

Ff

ork

fan

ox

ish

Directions: Have children name each picture and write the letter *f* to complete each word. Point to and say each word as children say it with you.

Help your child make up sentences using words that begin with the *f* sound, such as *Father finds a fish.*

Name ______________________________

Gg

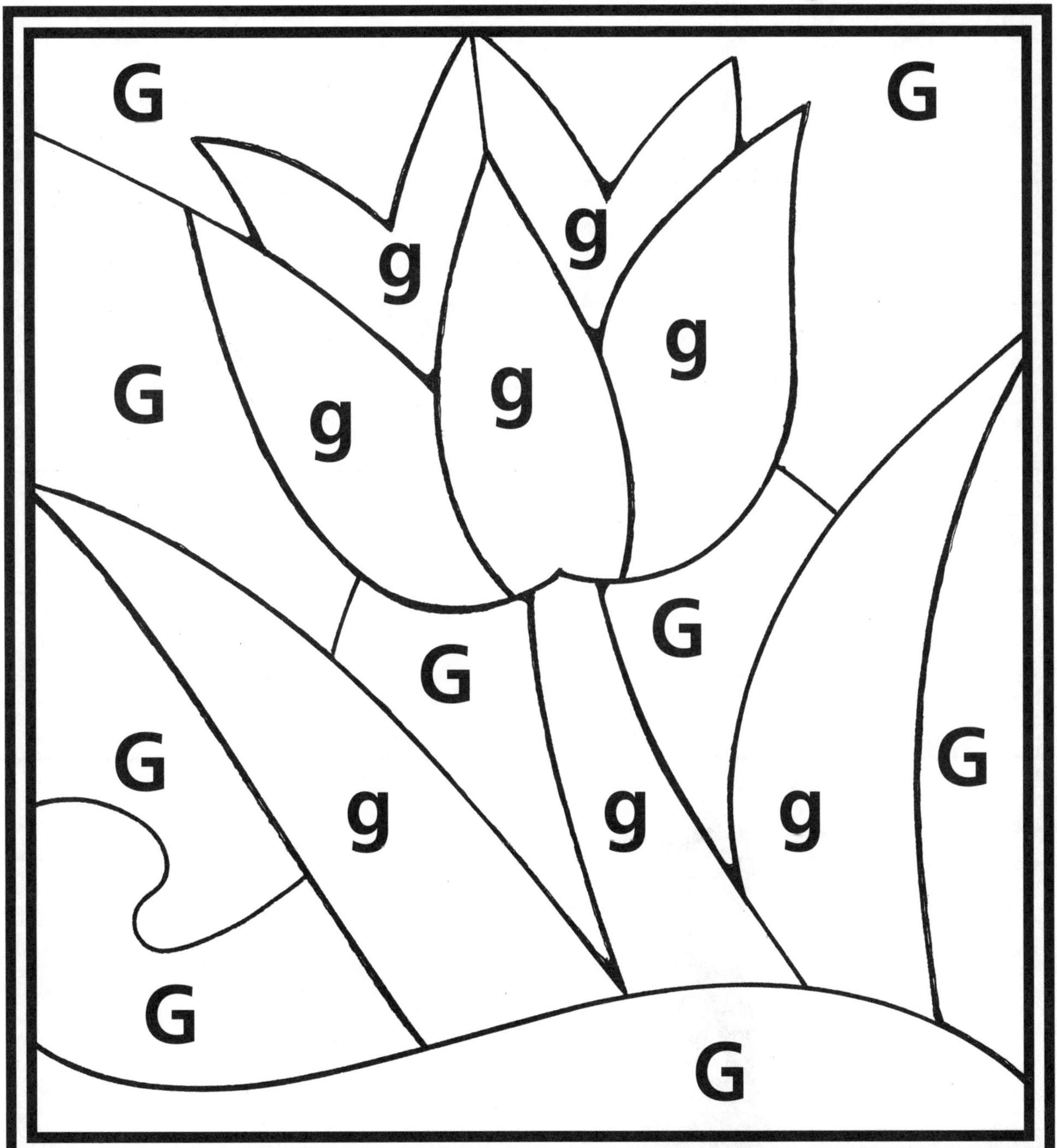

Directions: Help children find out what is growing in the garden. Have them use yellow to color the puzzle pieces with *G* and green to color the puzzle pieces with *g*.

Gg

GG

gg

Gg

girl

Directions: Have children trace the letters and write their own *G* and *g* on the lines. Then, have them identify the picture and complete the word.

HOME Have your child print large letters *G* and *g* on paper in a bright color with a crayon, marker, or finger paint.

Name ______________________

Gg 

Directions: Help children identify the pictures. If a picture name begins with the sound of *g*, have children circle the picture.

Gg

gg

Directions: Have children say each picture name. Have them color each picture whose name begins with /g/. Then, they can practice writing *g* on the line at the bottom of the page.

HOME Have your child write *Gg* on slips of paper and place them on things whose names begin with *g*.

Name ______________________________

Gg

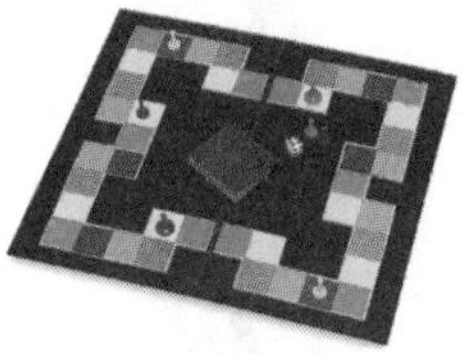

Directions: Help children name the pictures. If a picture name begins with the sound of *g*, have children print *Gg* on the line.

Gg

oat

game

irl

oose

Directions: Have children name each picture and write the letter *g* to complete each word. Point to and say each word as children say it with you.

HOME Help your child make up a sentence using each dictionary word, such as *Let's play a game.*

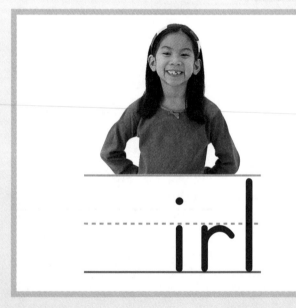

Name ______________________________

J

j f G

g

f J G

G

F g j

f

F G j

F

f J g

j

G f J

Directions: Have children draw a line to match the letter under the picture to its partner letter.

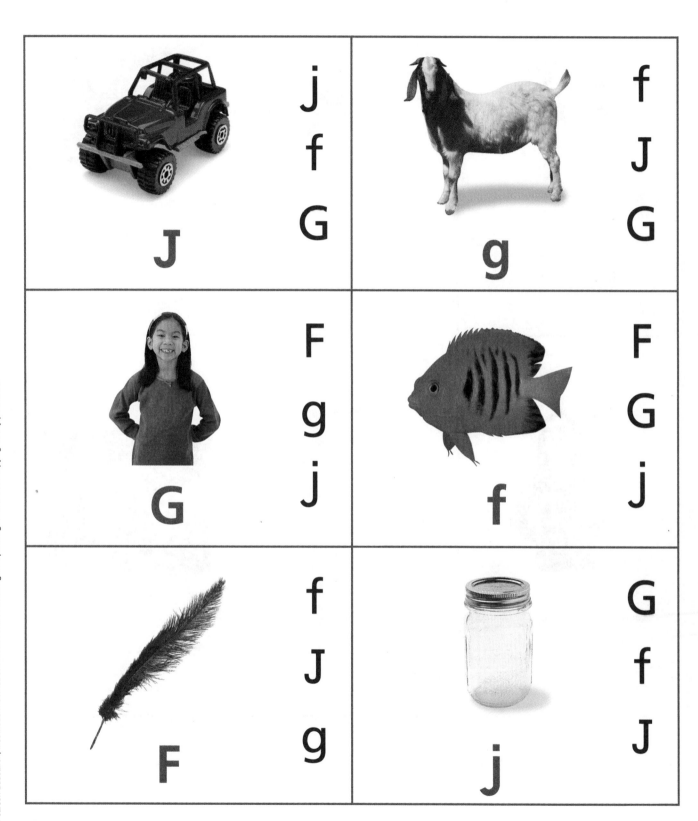

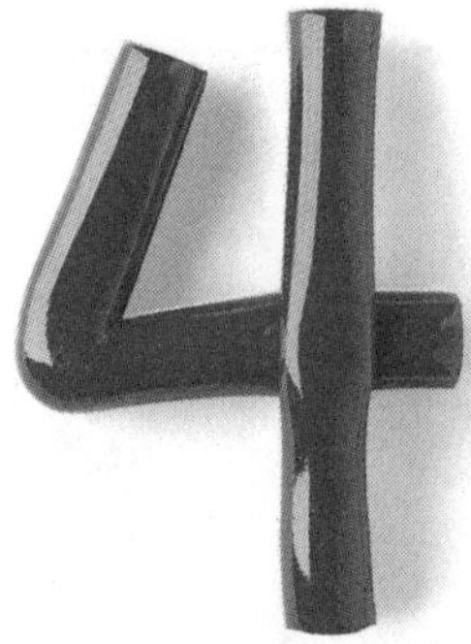

Ff

Directions: Help children name each picture. Then, have them trace or write the partner letters that stand for its beginning sound.

HOME Name an object that begins with *j*, *f*, or *g*. Have your child name the pictures on the page that begin with the same sound.

Name ______________________________

Directions: Say each picture name as children listen for the ending sound. Then have children color the pictures in each row whose names end with the same sound as the picture at the beginning of the row.

t m g

m t g

g m t

m g t

g t m

t g m

Directions: Say each picture name with children as they listen to the ending sound. Have children circle the letter that stands for the ending sound in each picture name.

HOME

Write words such as *hat*, *bug*, and *broom*, omitting the final *t*, *g*, and *m*. Help your child to complete each word and draw a picture.

Name ______________________________

s b

m t

j h

k b

g j

m f

h b

k f

s m

Directions: Help children say the name of each picture. Then, have them circle the letter that stands for the beginning sound.

UNIT 1 CHECKUP

 b m	 k h	 j b
 g s	 k t	 f h
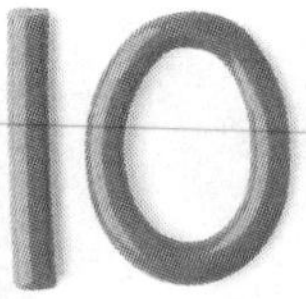 j t	 m f	 b g

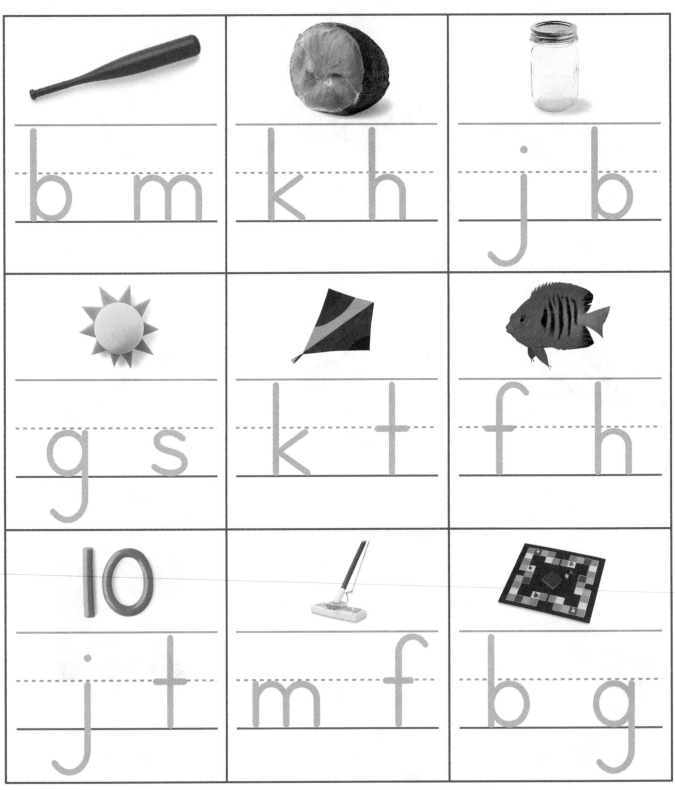

Directions: Have children name the pictures, then trace the letter that stands for the beginning sound.

HOME Ask your child to write the letters *b*, *h*, *j*, *s*, *k*, *f*, *t*, *m*, and *g* on slips of paper, then place them on things whose names begin with the letters.

Read Aloud

Always Be Kind to Animals

by John Gardner

Always be kind to animals,
Morning, noon, and night;
For animals have feelings too,
And furthermore, they bite.

TALK About It

What is your favorite animal?

HOME LETTER

Dear Family,

In this unit "Eyes on Animals," your child will learn to write the letters **l**, **d**, **n**, **w**, **c**, **r**, **p**, **q**, **v**, **y**, **x**, and **z**. Your child will also learn the sounds these letters make at the beginning of words and the sound of **x** at the end of words. As your child develops an understanding of these sounds, you may wish to try this activity.

- ▶ Help your child look through magazines for pictures of things whose names begin with letters they have learned. Cut out the pictures and place them in a paper bag. Then, have your child pull out the pictures one at a time, name the picture, and write the letter that begins the picture name.
- ▶ Animal names are a favorite way to help children learn beginning sounds and letters. Look for these books in your local library.

Mice Squeak We Speak
by Arnold Shapiro

Bringing the Rain to Kapiti Plain: A Nandi Tale
by Verna Aardema

Sincerely,

____

door

d

needle

n

Estimada familia:

En esta unidad, titulada "Una mirada a los animales" ("Animals"), su hijo/a aprenderá a escribir las letras **l**, **d**, **n**, **w**, **c**, **r**, **p**, **q**, **v**, **y**, **x**, **y**, **z**. También aprenderá los sonidos de estas letras al principio de palabras y el sonido de la x al final de palabras. A medida que su hijo/a se vaya familiarizando con estos sonidos, pueden hacer las siguientes actividades juntos.

- ▶ Ayuden a su hijo/a buscar en revistas ilustraciones de cosas cuyos nombres comienzan con las letras que ha aprendido. Recorten las ilustraciones y métanlas en una bolsa de papel. Después, pidan a su hijo/a que saque las ilustraciones una a una, la nombre y escriba la letra con la que comienza el nombre de la ilustración.
- ▶ Los nombres de animales son una manera favorita de ayudar a los niños en el aprendizaje de sonidos y letras al principio de palabras. Busquen estos libros en su biblioteca local.

Mice Squeak We Speak
de Arnold Shapiro

Bringing the Rain to Kapiti Plain: A Nandi Tale
de Verna Aardema

Sinceramente,

____

Name ______________________________

Ll

■ l	T	L	G
● L	l	j	f
▲ l	H	F	L
★ L	h	l	k

Directions: Have children identify the letter at the beginning of each row. Ask them to circle the letter in each row that is the partner letter.

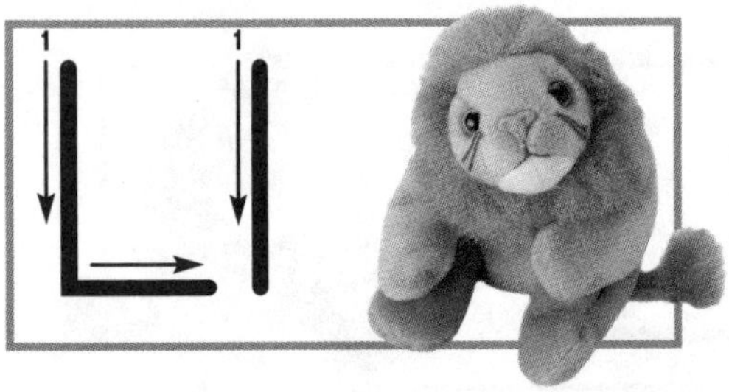

L L

l l

L l

lock

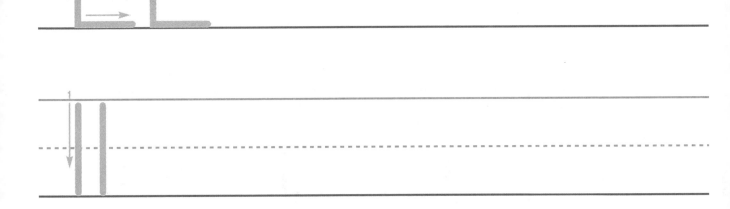

Directions: Have children trace the letters and write their own *L* and *l* on the lines. Then, have them identify the picture and complete the word.

HOME Have your child cut large letters *L* and *l* from construction paper and use crayons to fill the letters with colorful *Ll's*.

Name ______________________________

Ll

Directions: Help children identify the pictures. If a picture name begins with the sound of *l*, have children circle the picture.

Ll

Directions: Identify each picture. Have children color the boxes with pictures whose names begin with the *l* sound, then name the letter that appears. Then, have them practice writing *l* on the line at the bottom.

HOME Have your child print *L* on pieces of paper and place them on things whose names begin with *l*.

Name ______________________________

Ll 

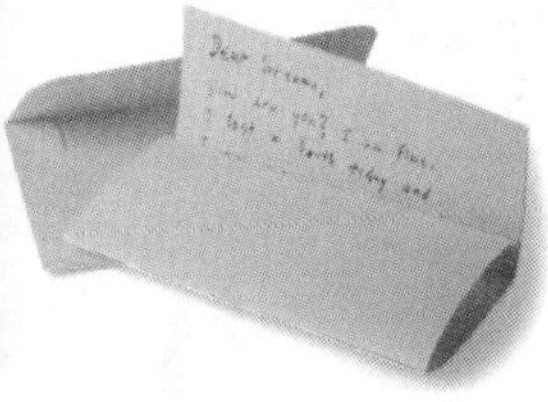

Directions: Help children name the pictures. If a picture name begins with the sound of *l*, have children print *Ll* on the line.

Ll

lamp

izard

eaf

og

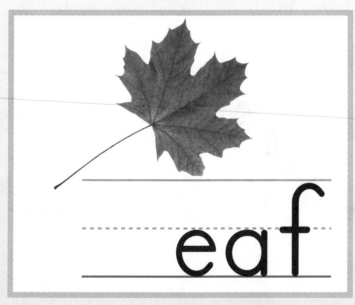

Directions: Have children name each picture and write the letter *l* to complete each word. Point to and say each word as children say it with you.

HOME Write the names of objects that begin with *l*, such as *ladder*, omitting the *l*. Ask your child to write the *l* and draw a picture.

Name ______________________________

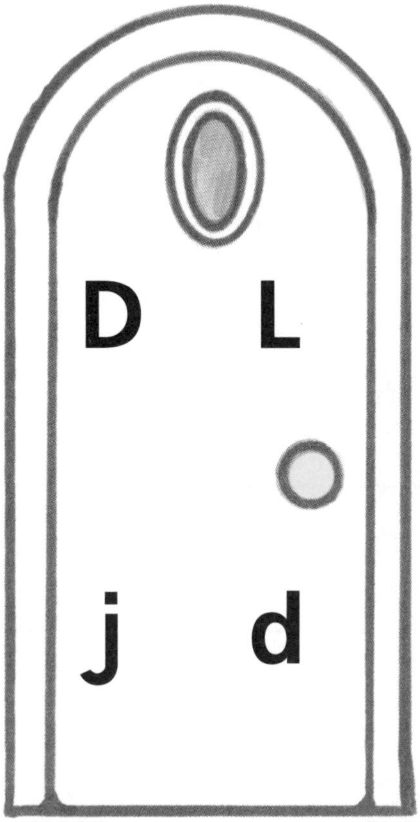

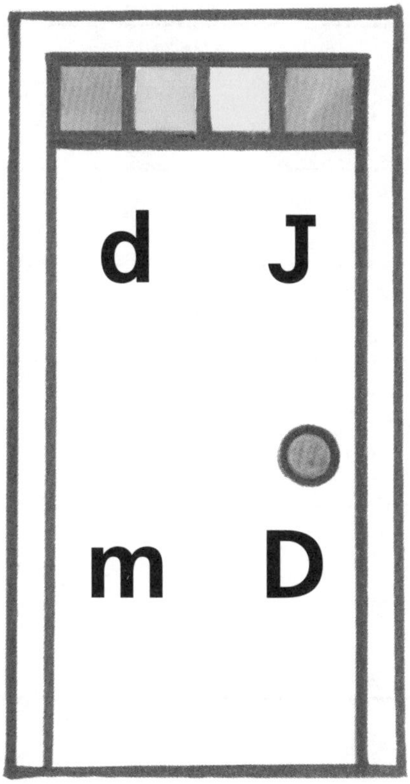

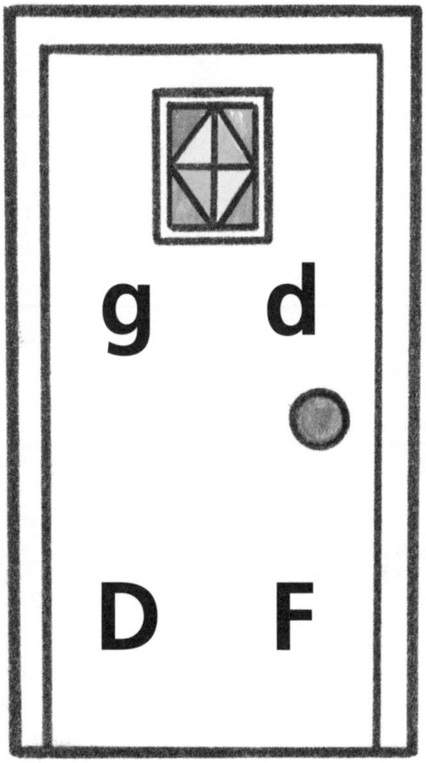

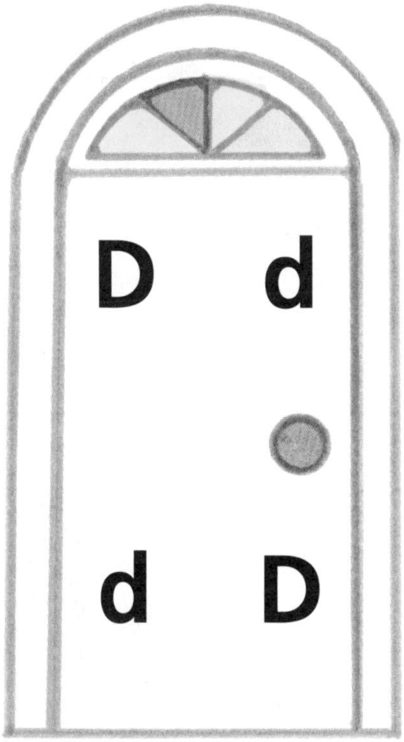

Directions: Have children identify the partner letters at the top of the page. Then, have them look at the letters on each door and draw a line to match the partner letters *D* and *d*. Ask them to color the door that shows only *D* and *d*.

DD

dd

Dd

dime

Directions: Have children trace the letters and write their own *D* and *d* on the lines. Then, have them identify the picture and complete the word.

HOME Invite your child to print *D* and *d*. Then write the words *dog* and *dime*, omitting the *d's*. Have your child complete the words.

Name ______________________________

Dd

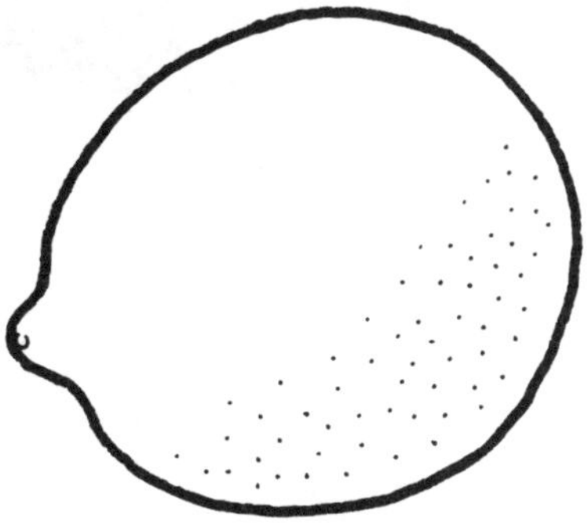

Directions: Help children identify the pictures. If a picture name begins with the sound of *d*, have children color the picture.

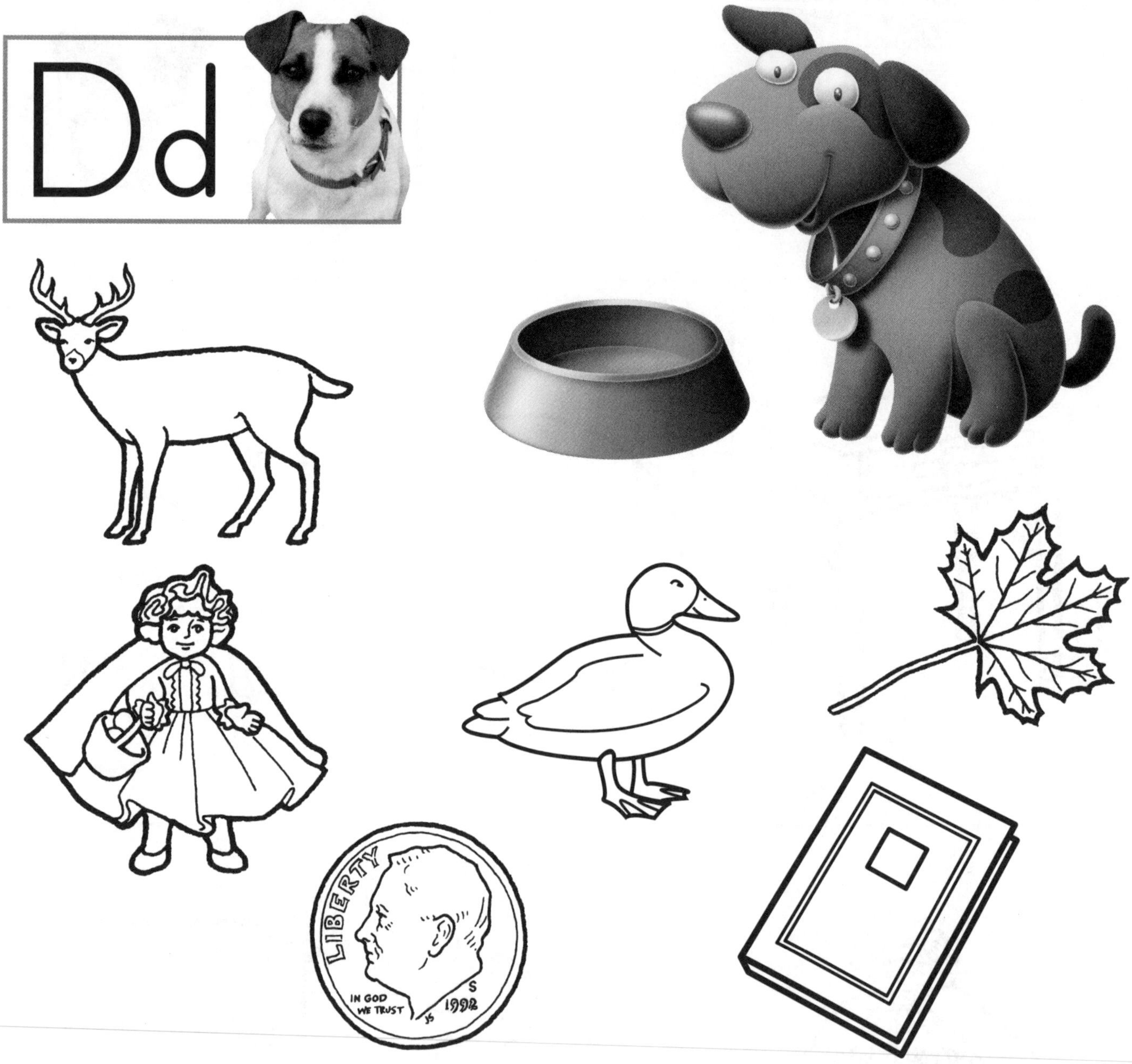

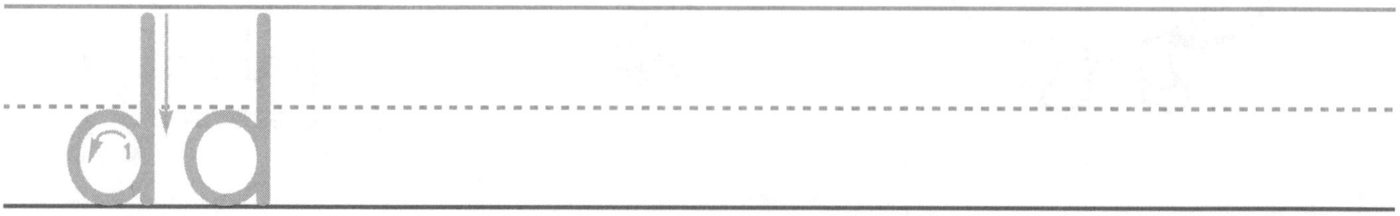

Directions: Help children identify each picture. Have them color the pictures whose names begin with the sound of *d*. Then have them practice writing *d* on the line at the bottom of the page.

HOME Write the name of each picture your child colored, omitting the *d*. Have your child print *d* to complete each word. Read the words.

Name ____________________

Nn

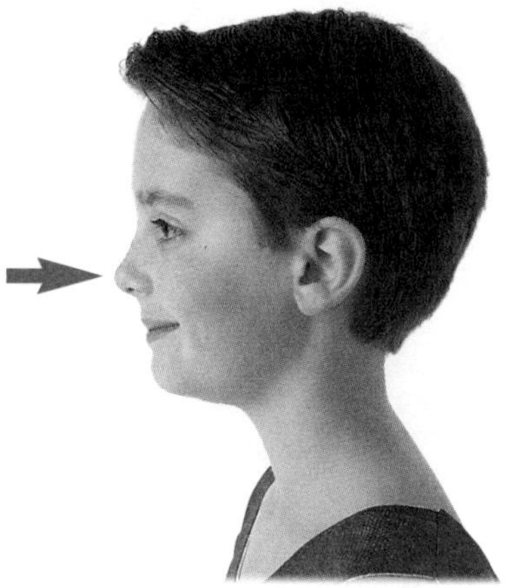

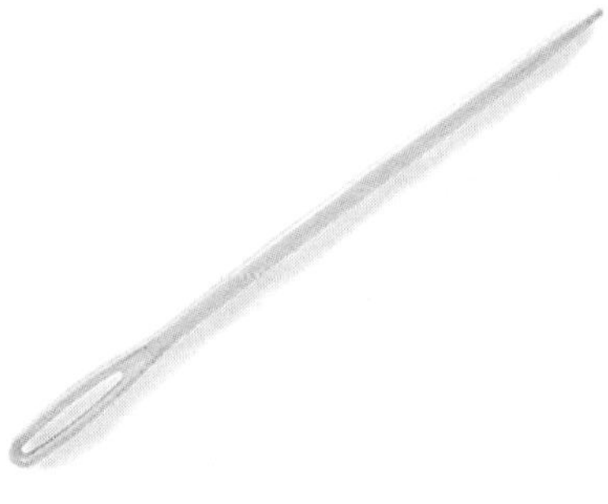

Directions: Help children identify the pictures. If a picture name begins with the sound of *n*, have children circle the picture.

Nn 

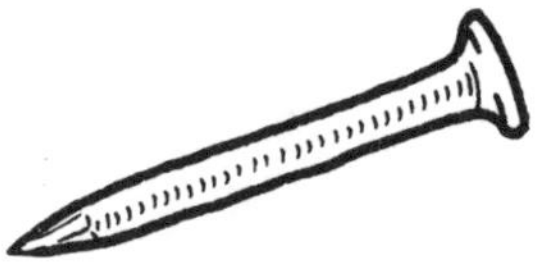

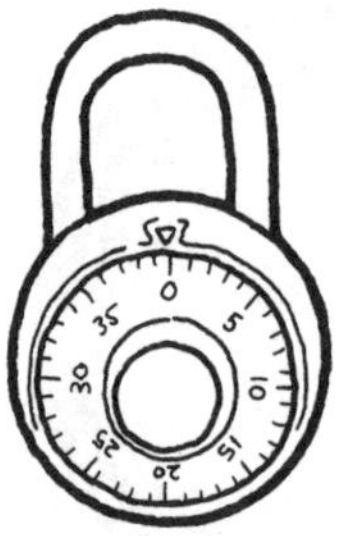

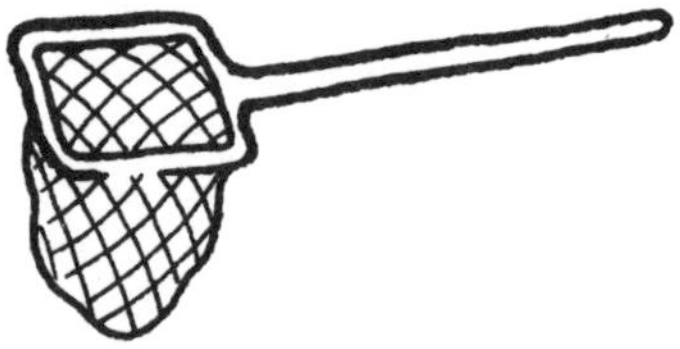

Directions: Ask children to color each thing with a name that begins with the sound of *n*. Help children name the three workers. Then, have them draw a line from each object they colored to the worker who would use it.

HOME Write names and words with *N* such as *Nick*, *Ned*, *Nan*, *nap*, and *nine*, omitting the *N* and *n*. Have your child print *N* and *n* to finish the names.

Name ______________________

Nn 

Directions: Help children name the pictures. If a picture name begins with the sound of *n*, have children print *Nn* on the line.

Nn 

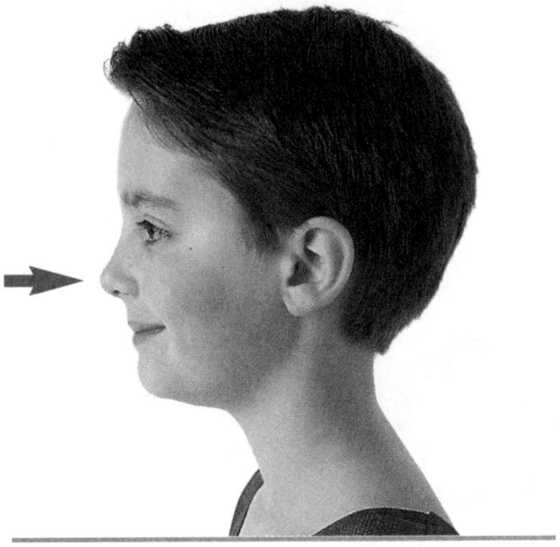

ose

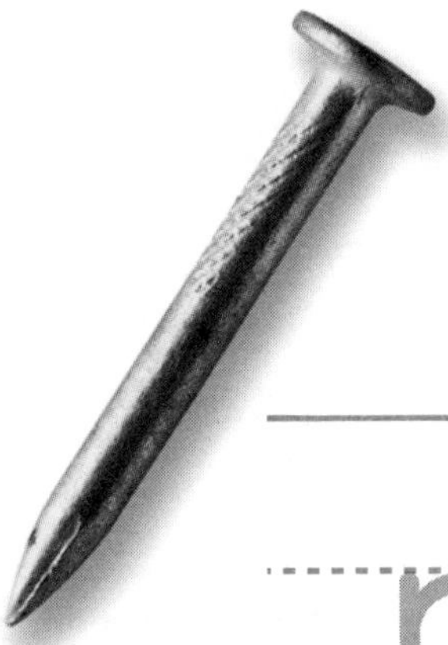

nail

eedle

urse

Directions: Have children name each picture and write the letter *n* to complete each word. Point to and say each word as children say it with you.

HOME Help your child make up sentences using words that begin with the *n* sound, such as *Nurses need naps.*

Name ______________________________

 N d l L	 l D n d
 n d L N	 N d l L
 L n d D	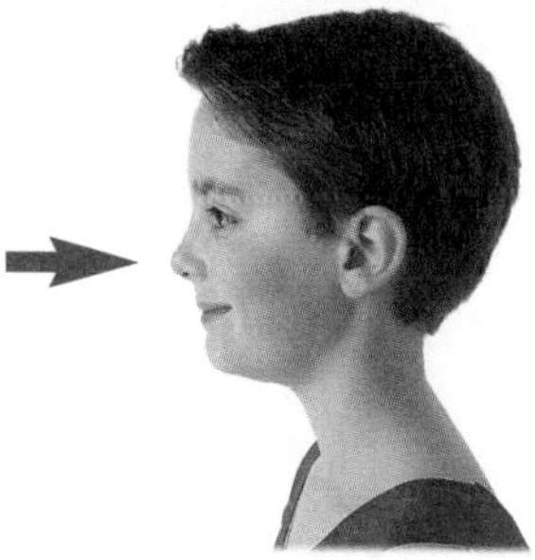 N D l n

Directions: Have children draw a line to match the letter under the picture to its partner letter.

Nn

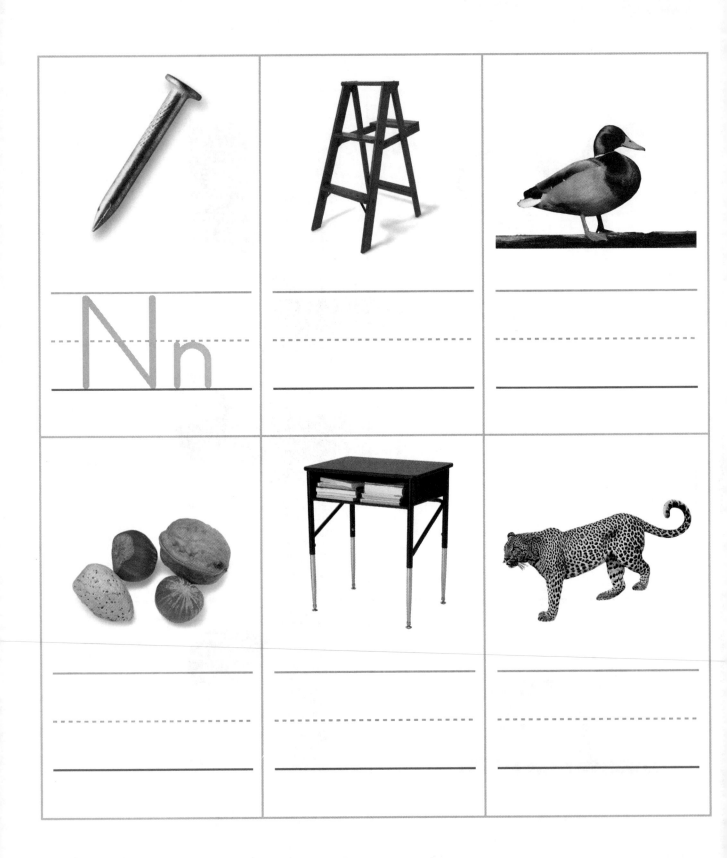

Directions: Have children name each picture and then trace or write the partner letters that stand for its beginning sound.

Name a word that begins with *l*, *d*, or *n*. Have your child name another word that begins with the same sound.

Name ______________________

I	**have**
go	**to**

■ I go to a  .

● I have a 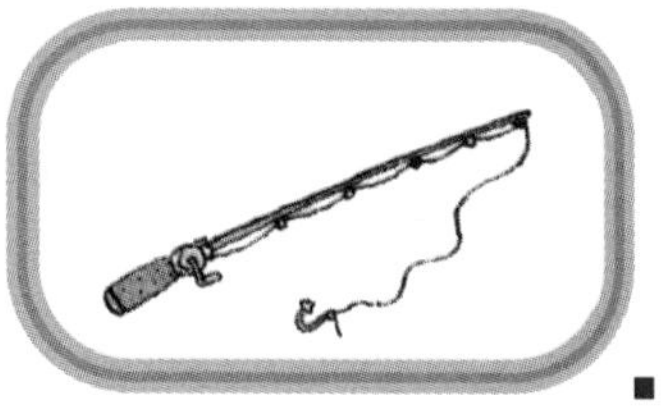 .

▲ I have a 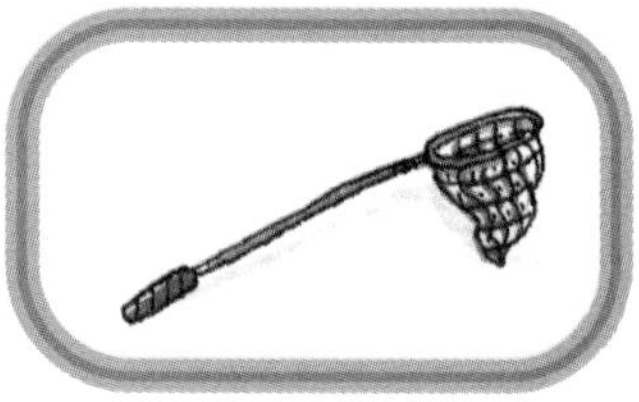 .

★ I go to  .

Directions: Read the words in the box and have children repeat them. Invite children to say and trace the word in each sentence. Then, read the sentences with children.

I	have
go	to

■ I go to a .

● I have a .

▲ I have a 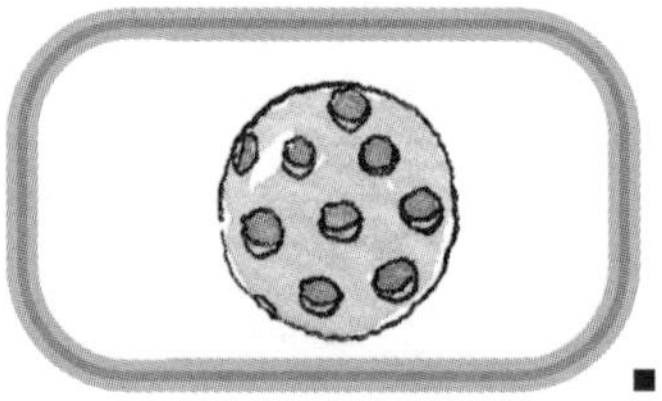.

★ I go to .

Directions: Help children to read each sentence. Then, have them trace each word to complete the sentence. Invite them to read the sentence again.

HOME Write the words from this lesson on paper. Have your child copy and read the words.

I have lips to smile.

4

Name ____________________

All About Me

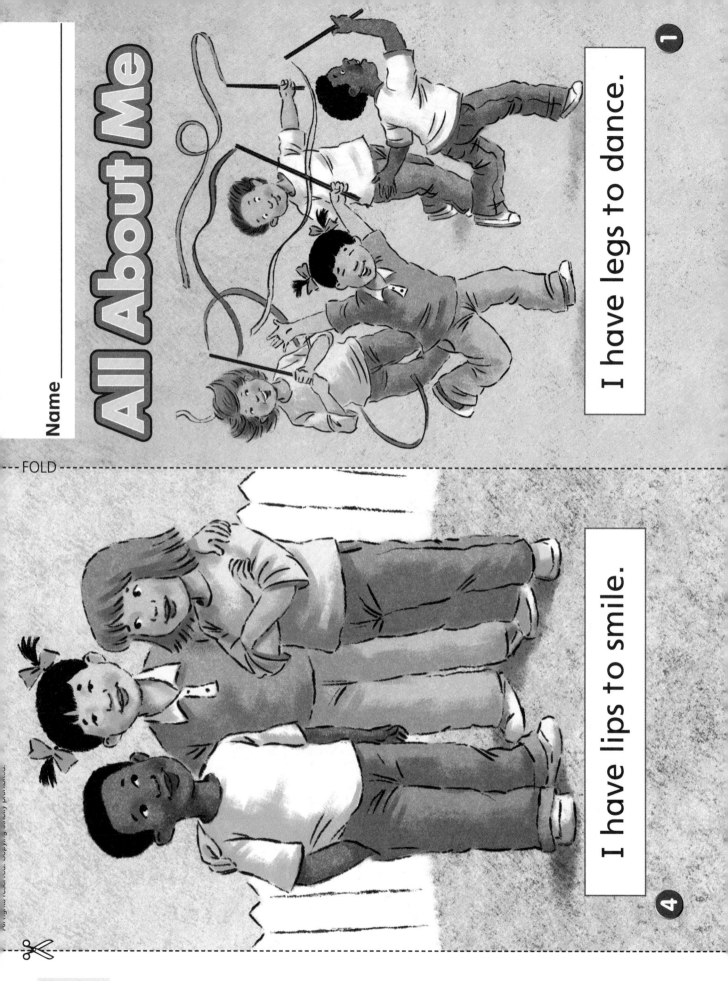

I have legs to dance.

1

FOLD

Directions: Read the story aloud, and discuss the pictures with children.

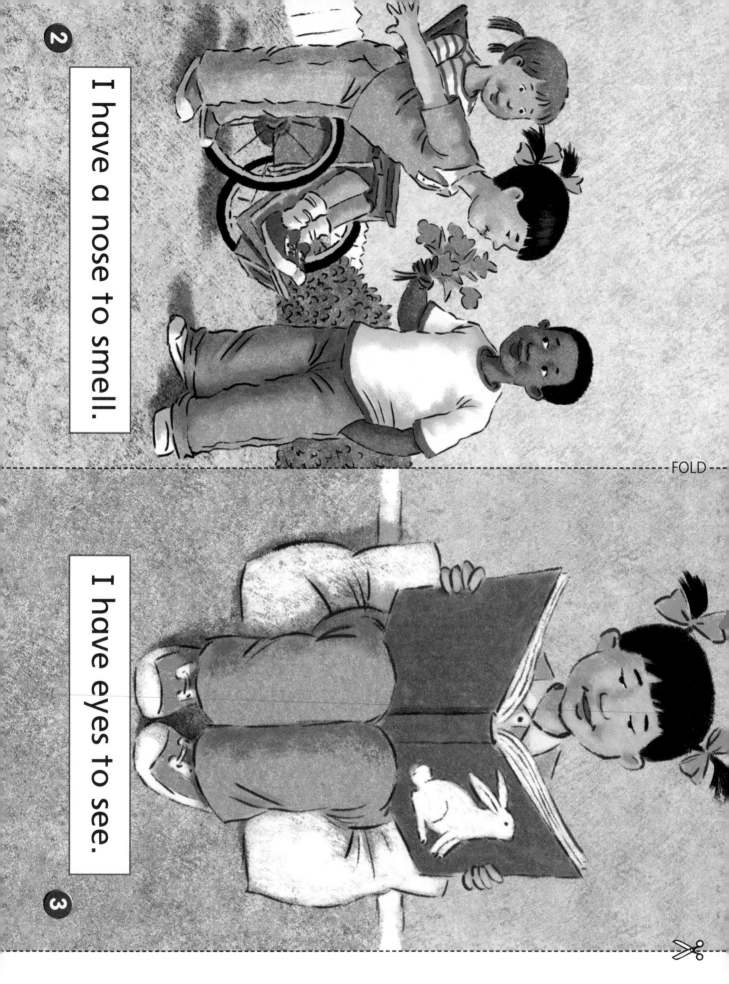

I have a nose to smell.

2

FOLD

I have eyes to see.

3

Name ______________________________

Directions: Have children identify the partner letters at the top of the page. Then have children draw lines to connect alternating letters *W* and *w* to show the path to get the walrus back to the ocean.

Ww

W W

w w

W w

wagon

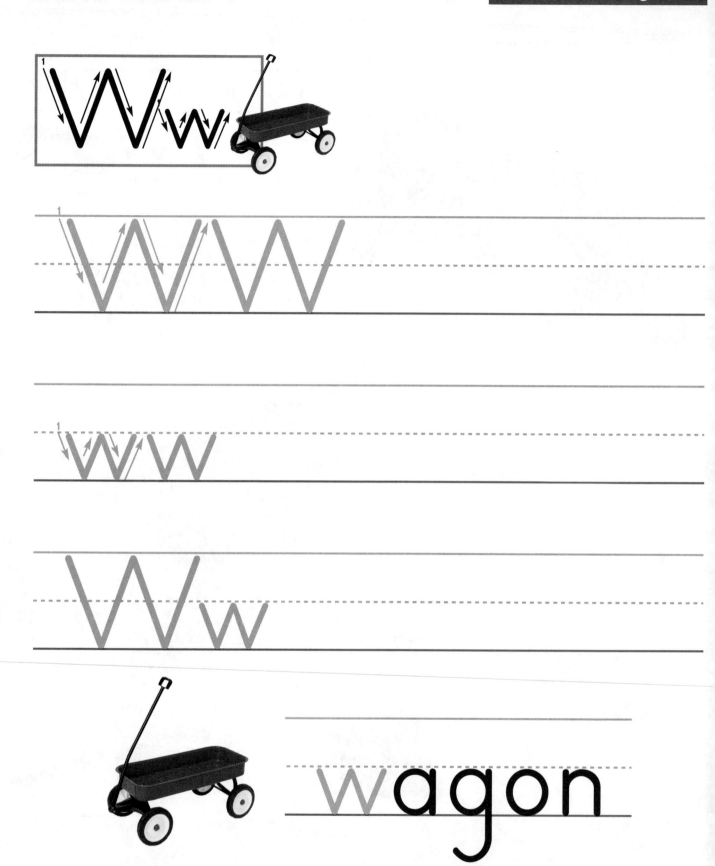

Directions: Have children trace the letters and write their own *W* and *w* on the lines. Then, have them identify the picture and complete the word.

HOME Have your child draw a wagon and print several *W's* and *w's* inside. Write the word *web*, omitting the *w*. Have your child complete the word.

Name ______________________________

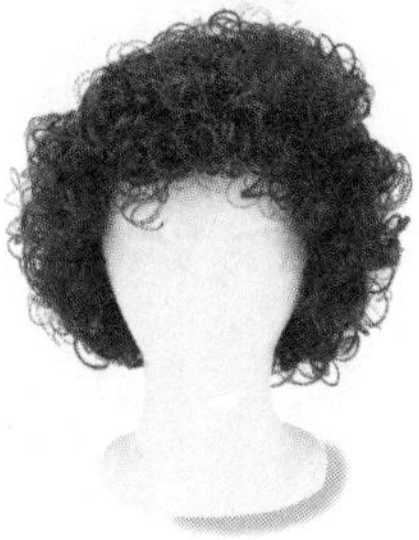 ______________________

 ______________________

 ______________________

 ______________________

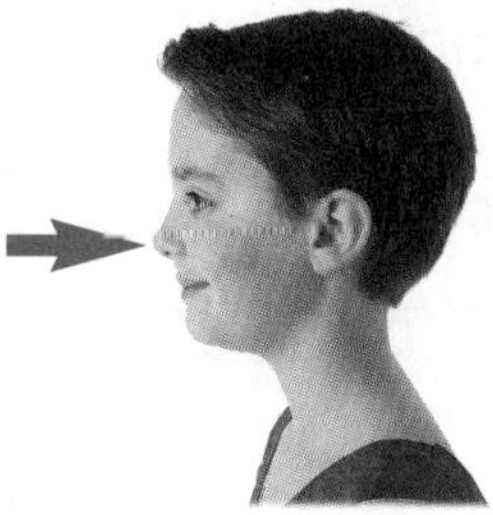 ______________________

 ______________________

Directions: Help children name the pictures. If a picture name begins with the sound of *w*, have children print *Ww* on the line.

ing

web

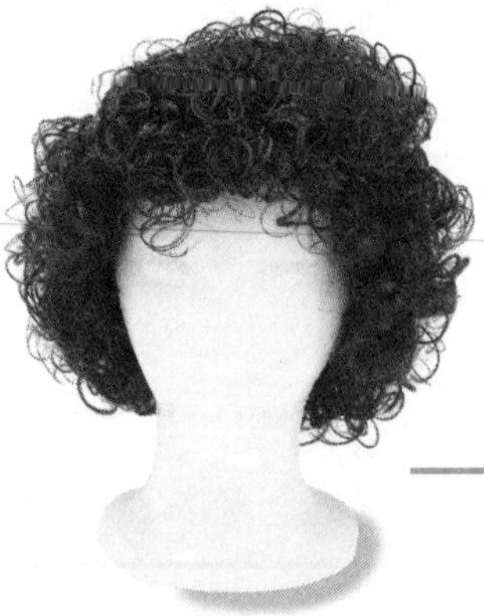

ig

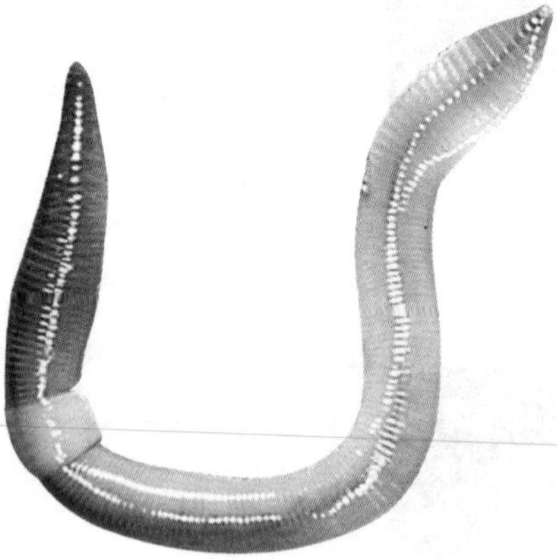

orm

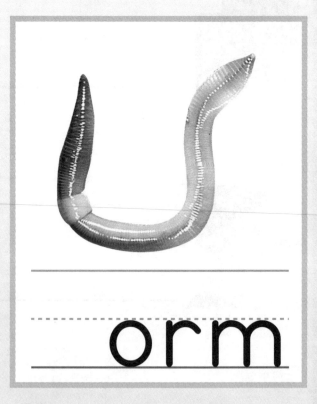

Directions: Have children name each picture and write the letter *w* to complete each word. Point to and say each word as children say it with you.

HOME

Help your child make up sentences using words that begin with the *w* sound, such as *Watch Willy Worm wiggle*.

Name ______________________________

Cc

■ c	W	C	D
● C	n	l	c
▲ C	c	f	m
★ c	G	C	D

Directions: Have children identify the letter at the beginning of each row. Ask them to circle the letter in each row that is the partner letter.

Cc

C C

c c

C c

cow

Directions: Have children trace the letters and write their own *C* and *c* on the lines. Then, have them identify the picture and complete the word.

HOME Have your child write *C* and *c* on slips of paper and match the letters to the same letters on food labels found in your kitchen.

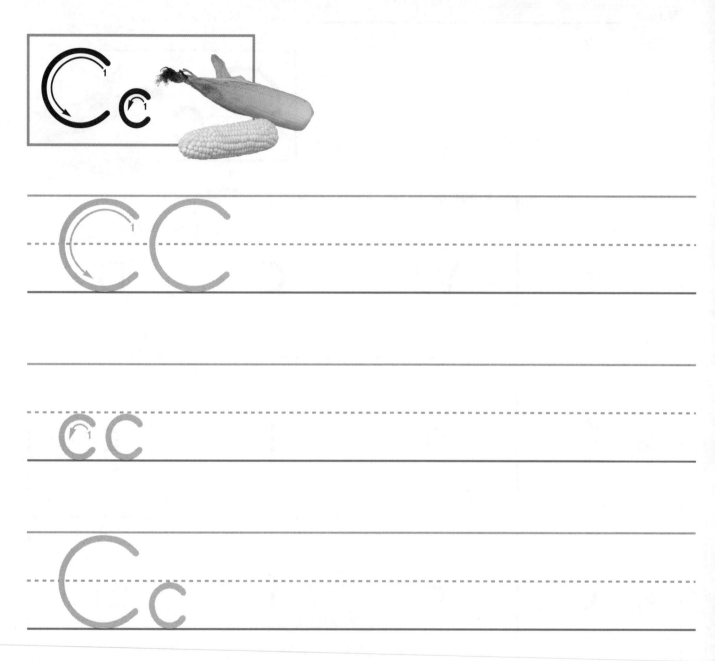

Name ______________________________

Cc

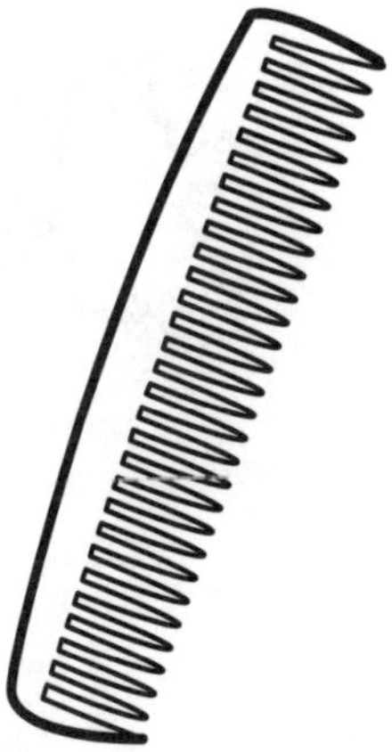

Directions: Help children identify the pictures. If a picture name begins with the sound of *c*, have children color the picture.

Cc

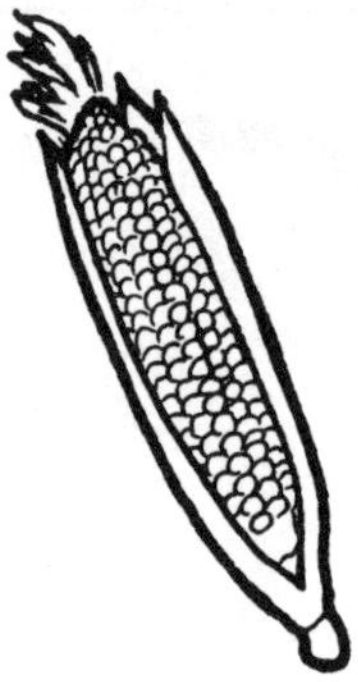

C c

Directions: Help children name the pictures of food. Then have them color each food that begins with the sound of *c*. Encourage them to practice writing *c* on the line at the bottom of the page.

HOME Write the words *cream corn*, *carrot cake*, *coconut cookies*, omitting the *c's*. Have your child print *c* to finish each word, then draw a picture.

Name ____________________

Cc

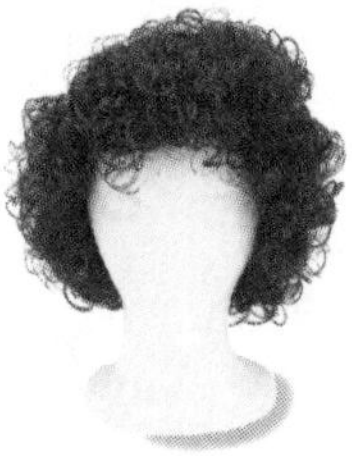

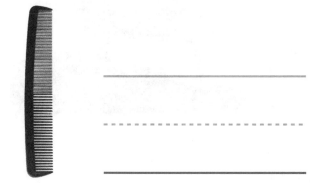

Directions: Help children name the pictures. If a picture name begins with the sound of *c*, have children print *Cc* on the line.

Cc

oat

cap

ar

ow

Directions: Have children name each picture and write the letter *c* to complete each word. Point to and say each word as children say it with you.

HOME Help your child make up sentences using words from the picture dictionary or other words they know that begin with the sound of *c*.

Name ______________________________

Directions: Have children identify the partner letters at the top of the page. Then, have them draw a line to connect the alternating letters *R* and *r* to help the rabbit get to its home.

Rr

RR

rr

Rr

ring

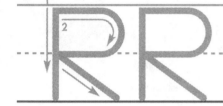

Directions: Have children trace the letters and write their own *R* and *r* on the lines. Then, have them identify the picture and complete the word.

HOME Invite your child to draw a rabbit and print *R* and *r* inside it. Write the word *rabbit*, omitting the *r*. Have your child finish the word.

Name ______________________________

Rr

Directions: Help children identify the pictures. If a picture name begins with the sound of *r*, have children circle the picture.

Rr

r r

Directions: Help children name the pictures shown on the books, circle each book with a picture that begins with *r*, and draw a line from the book to the children. Then, have them practice writing *r* on the line at the bottom of the page.

HOME Have your child write *R* and *r* on pieces of paper, then place them on things whose names begin with *r*.

Name ______________________

Rr

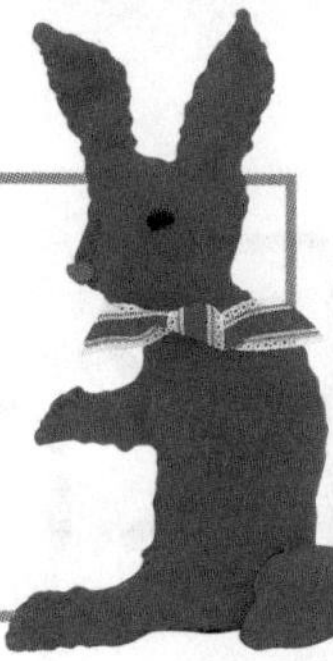

Directions: Help children name the pictures. If a picture name begins with the sound of *r*, have children print *Rr* on the line.

Rr

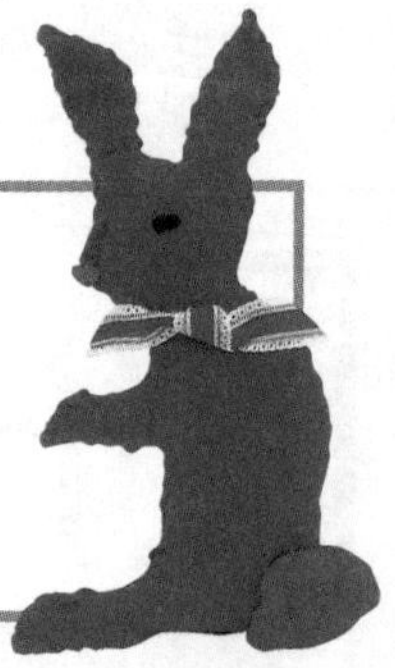

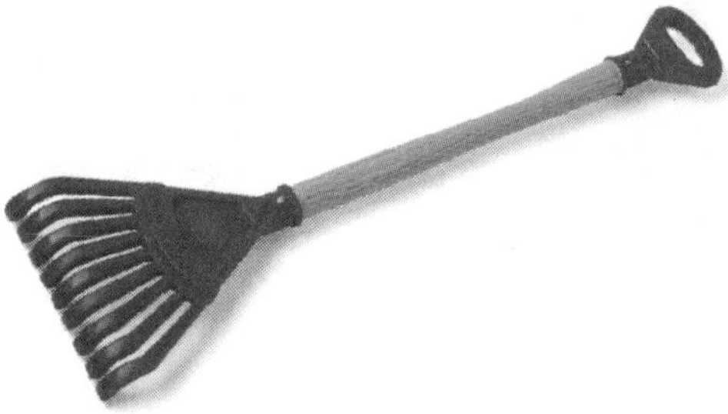

rake

ock

ope

uler

Directions: Have children name each picture and write the letter *r* to complete each word. Point to and say each word as children say it with you.

HOME Help your child make up sentences telling about things they can do with each item from the picture dictionary.

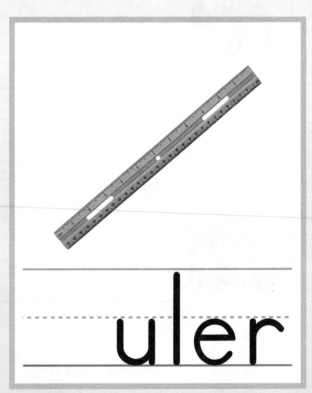

Name ______________________________

 W — C w r	 r — W R c
 C — c R w	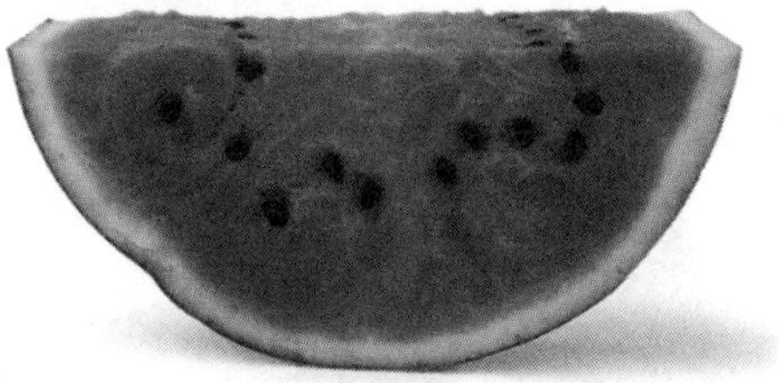 w — c R W
 R — C w r	 c — R C w

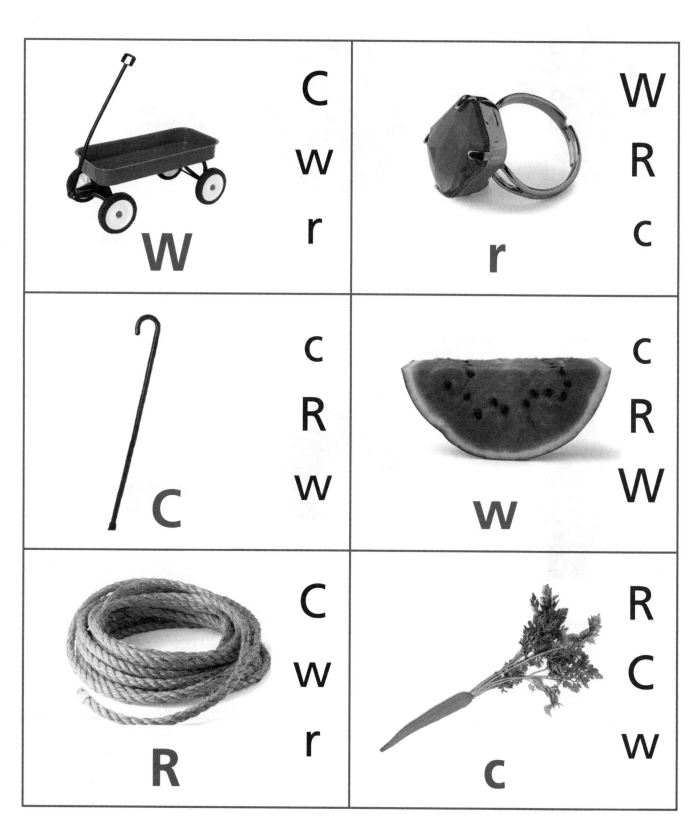

Directions: Have children draw a line to match the letter under the picture to its partner letter.

C c

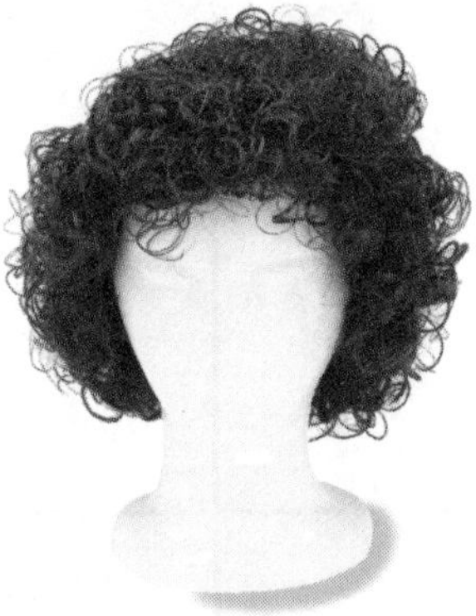

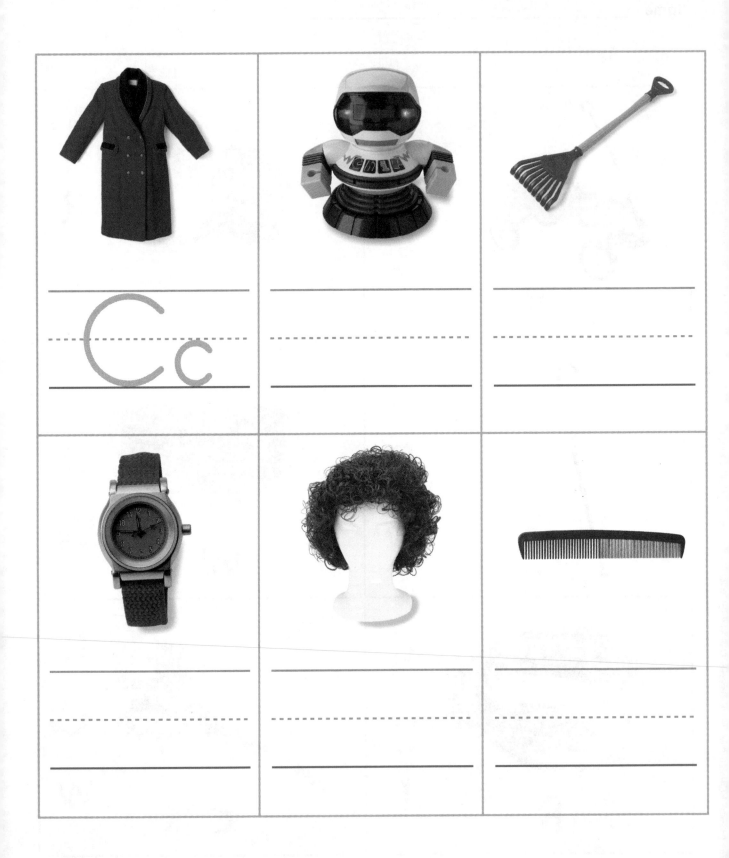

Directions: Help children name each picture, and then trace or print the partner letters that stand for its beginning sound.

HOME Have your child print the letters *w*, *c*, *r*. Point to a letter and have your child name words that begin with the letter.

Name ______________________________

Directions: Have children identify the partner letters at the top of the page. Then, have children trace a path with crayon through the alternating partner letters *P* and *p* to help the pig get to its pen.

Pp

P P

p p

P p

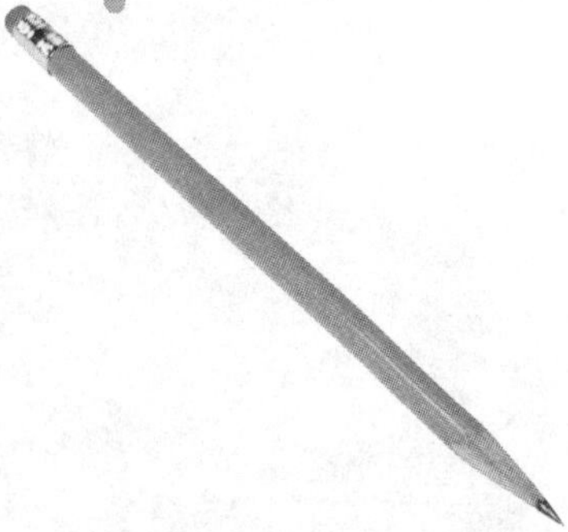

pencil

Directions: Have children trace the letters and print their own *P* and *p* on the lines. Then, have them identify the picture and complete the word.

HOME

Write the letters *B, P, R, p, d, b*. Have your child find and trace *P* and *p*, using a purple crayon, and then print *P* and *p*.

Name ______________________________

Pp

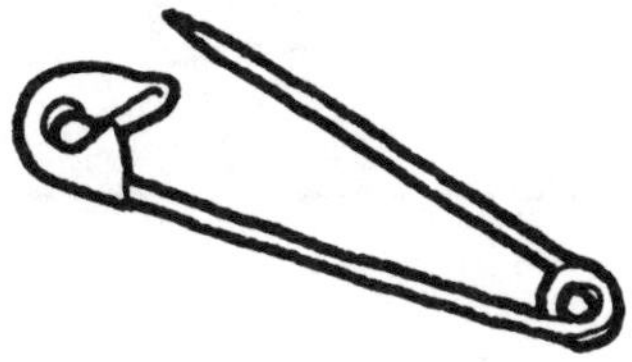		

Directions: Help children identify the pictures. If a picture name begins with the sound of *p*, have children color the picture.

Pp

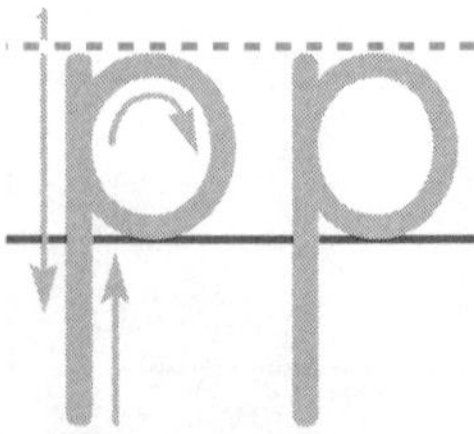

Directions: Help children name each picture. Then, have them color each picture whose name begins with *p*. Encourage them to practice printing *p* on the line.

HOME Have your child print *Pp* on slips of paper and place them on things whose names begin with *p*, such as a *pan*, a *pillow*, or in a *pocket*.

Name ______________________________

Qq

■ q	Q	c	p
● Q	c	r	q
▲ q	P	Q	W
★ Q	r	d	q

Directions: Have children identify the letter at the beginning of each row. Ask them to circle the letter in each row that is the partner letter.

Qq

Q Q

q q

Q q

quilt

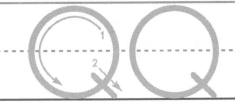

Directions: Have children trace the letters and print their own *Q* and *q* on the lines. Then, have them identify the picture and complete the word.

HOME Write the words *quick* and *quiet*, omitting the *qs*. Invite your child to complete them by printing Q and q.

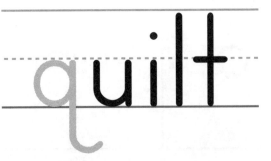

Name ______________________________

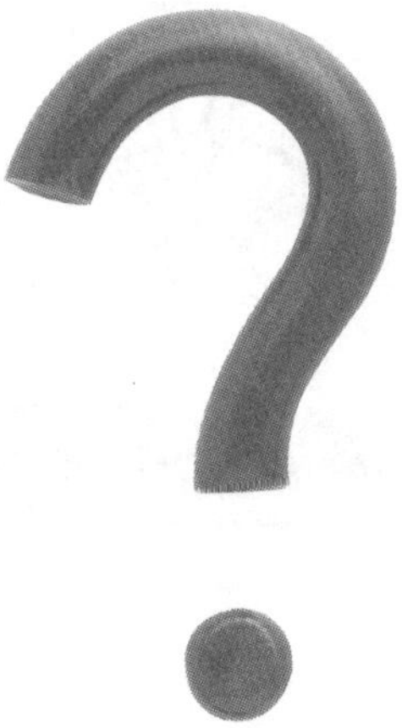

Directions: Help children identify the pictures. If a picture name begins with the sound of */kw/q*, have children circle the picture.

Qq

q q

Directions: Help children name the pictures on the quilt. Have them color each quilt square with a picture name that begins with the sound of /kw/*q*. Then have them practice printing the letter *q*.

HOME Say words that begin with *p* and *q*. Have your child repeat the words and print *Qq* each time a word begins with that letter sound.

Name ____________________

Qq

Directions: Help children name the pictures. If a picture name begins with the sound of */kw/q*, have children print *Qq* on the line.

Qq

quarter

uiet

ueen

uilt

Directions: Have children name each picture and print the letter *q* to complete each word. Point to and say each word as children say it with you.

HOME Have your child point to each dictionary word and say a sentence using the word, such as: *The queen is wearing a crown.*

Name ______________________________

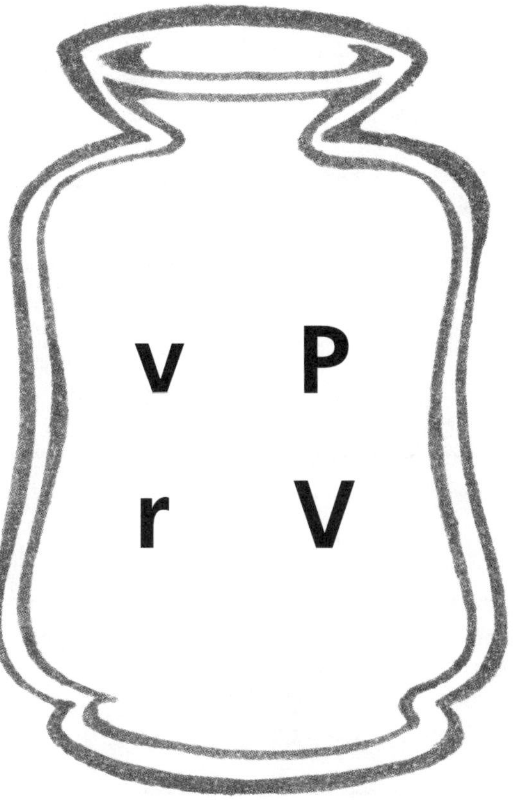

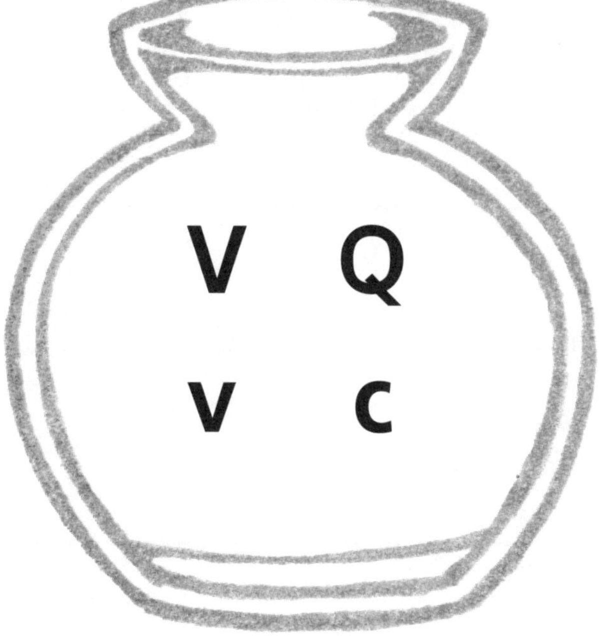

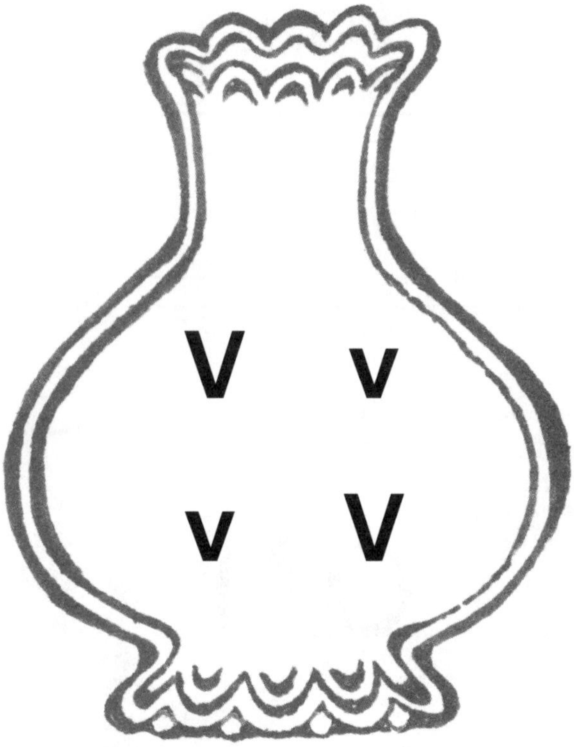

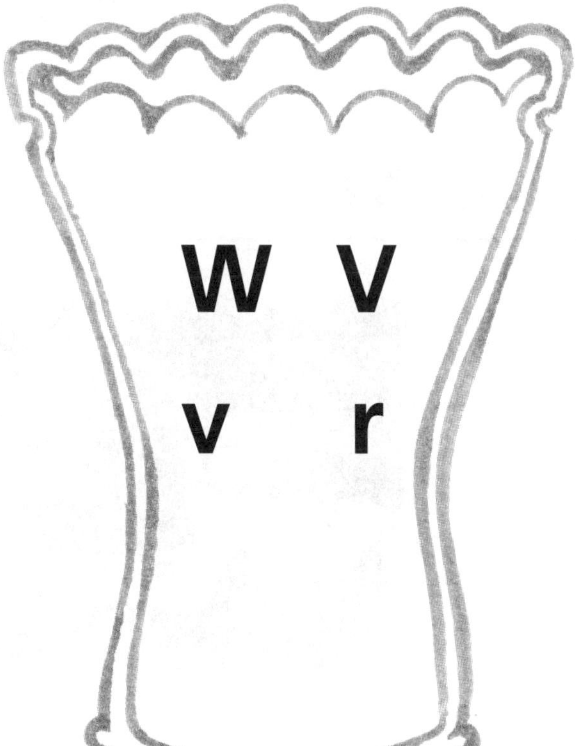

Directions: Have children identify the partner letters at the top of the page. Then, have them draw a line to match the partner letters *V* and *v* on each vase. Ask them to color the vase that shows only *V* and *v*.

Vv

V V

v v

V v

van

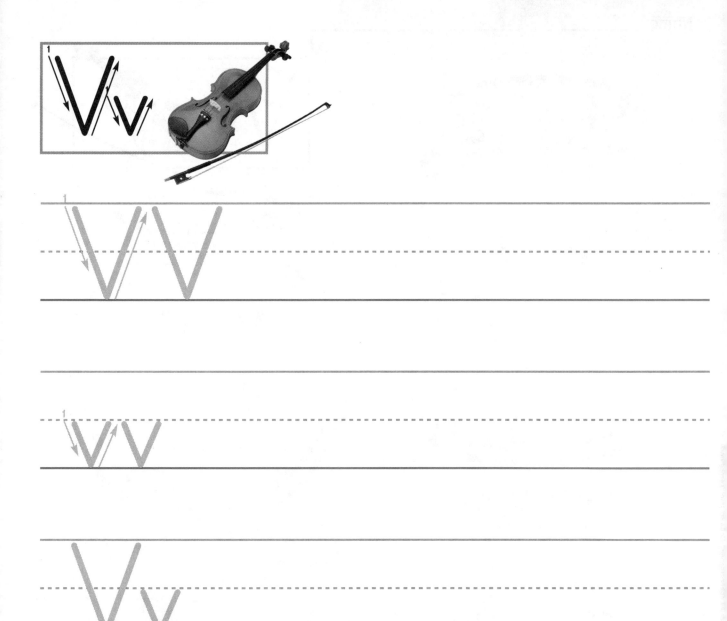

Directions: Have children trace the letters and print their own *V* and *v* on the lines. Then, have them identify the picture and complete the word.

HOME Invite your child to print *V* and *v*. Write words *vase* and *van*, omitting the *v's*, for your child to complete and draw a picture.

Name ______________________________

Vv

 ______________________

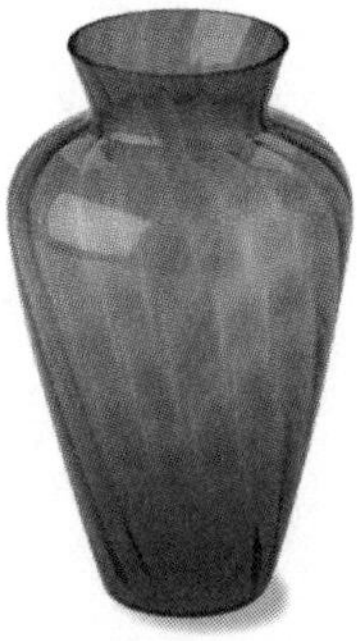 ______________________

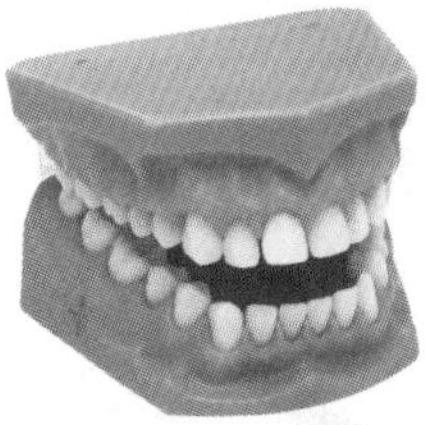 ______________________

____

 ______________________

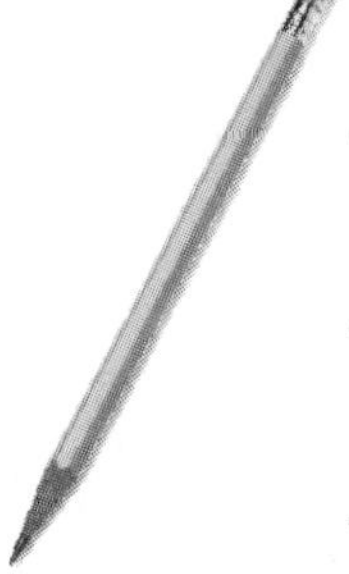 ______________________

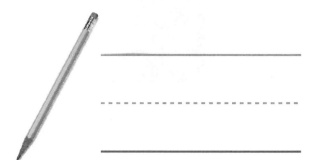

Directions: Help children name the pictures. If a picture name begins with the sound of *v*, have children print *Vv* on the line.

Vv

ine

vase

est

iolin

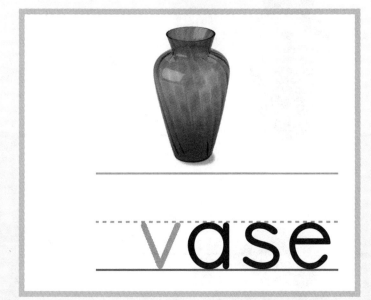

Directions: Have children name each picture and print the letter *v* to complete each word. Point to and say each word as children say it with you.

HOME Help your child make up sentences using words that begin with *v*, such as *Valerie's vest is violet.*

Name ______________________________

P

Q
p
v

v

V
q
P

Q

p
V
q

p

Q
P
v

V

P
q
v

q

p
Q
V

Directions: Help children identify each picture. Have children draw a line to match the letter under the picture to its partner letter.

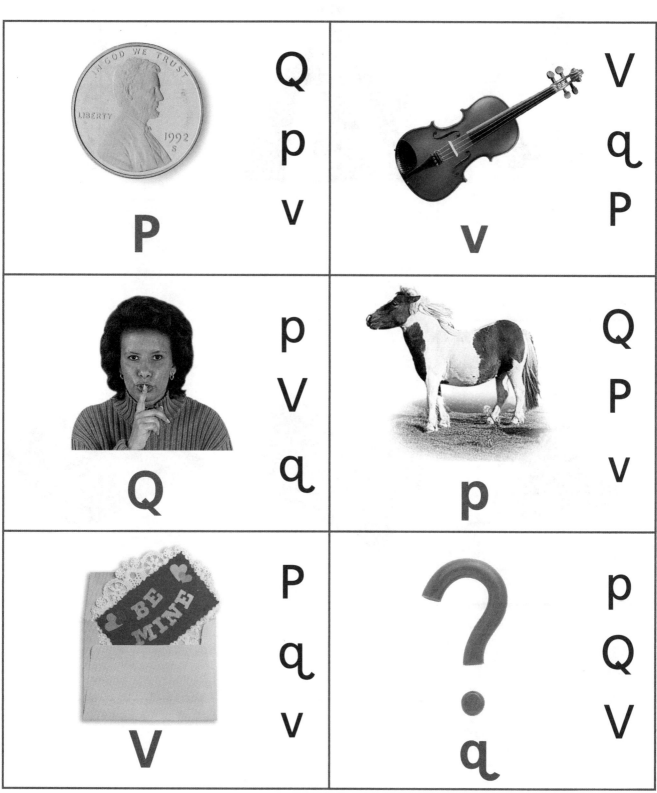

Pp

Directions: Have children name each picture, and then trace or write the partner letters that stand for its beginning sound.

Have your child name the two pictures that begin with the same sound, then name other words that begin with *p*, *q*, or *v*.

Name ______________________

It See
like do

■ I like to  .

● I do it at the  .

▲ It is fun to do.

★ See my 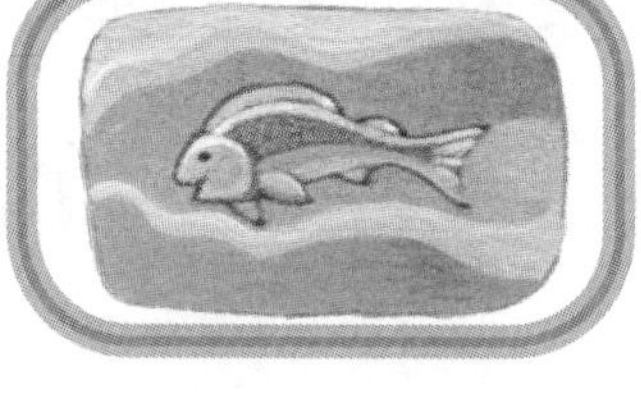 !

Directions: Help children to read the words in the box and to read each sentence. Have them trace each word to complete the sentence. Then, help them to read the sentences again.

Name ______________________________

it see
like do

■ I see a  .

● It has  on it.

▲ I know what to do.

★ I like to  .

Directions: Help children to read each sentence. Then, have them trace each word to complete the sentence. Invite them to read the sentence again.

HOME Have your child help print two sets of the words on slips of paper. Mix up the words for your child to match and read

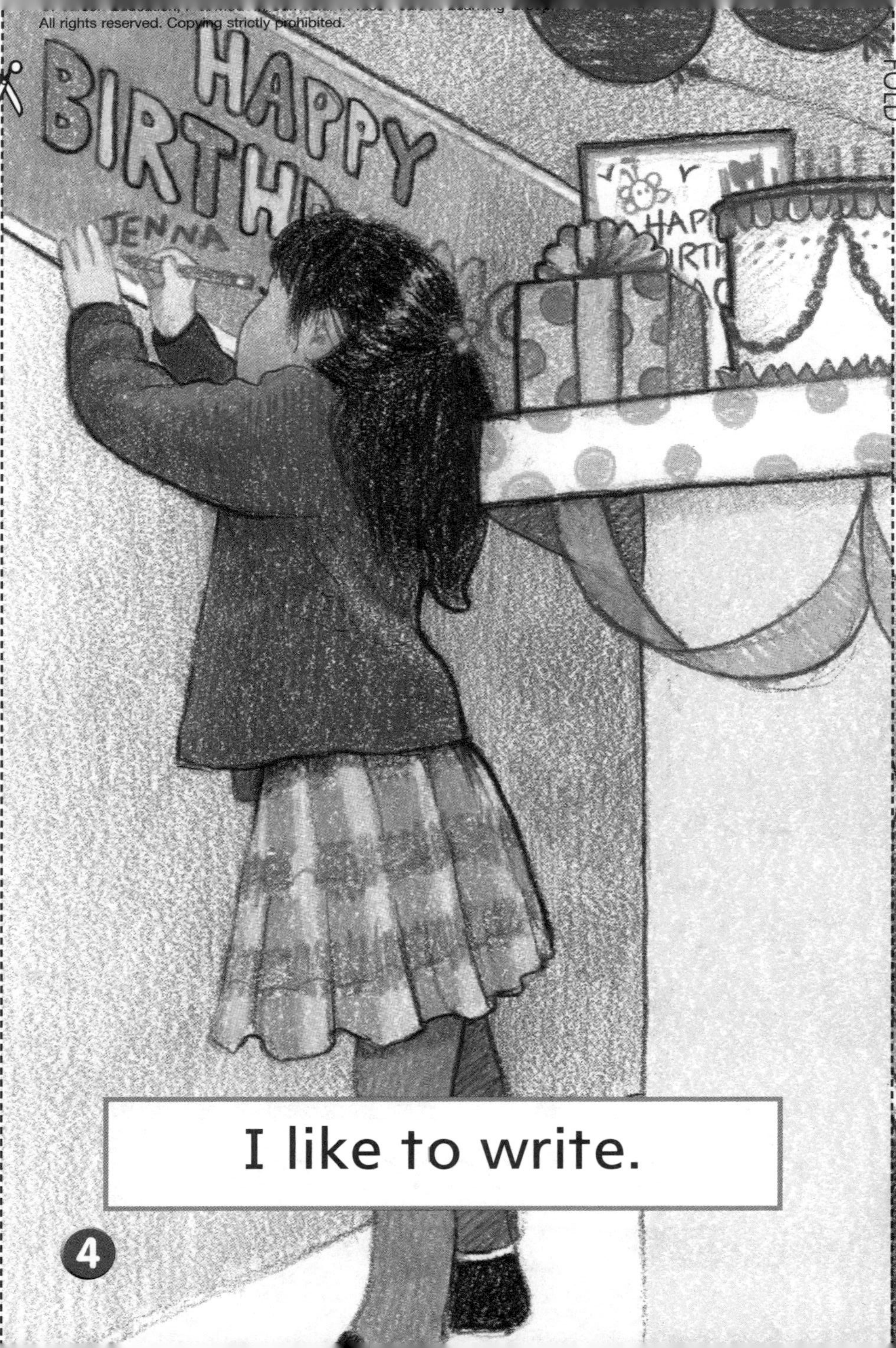

I like to write.

4

FOLD

Name ______________________

See Me Write!

See me write!

1

Directions: Read the story aloud, and discuss the pictures with children.

2

I do it on the card.

FOLD

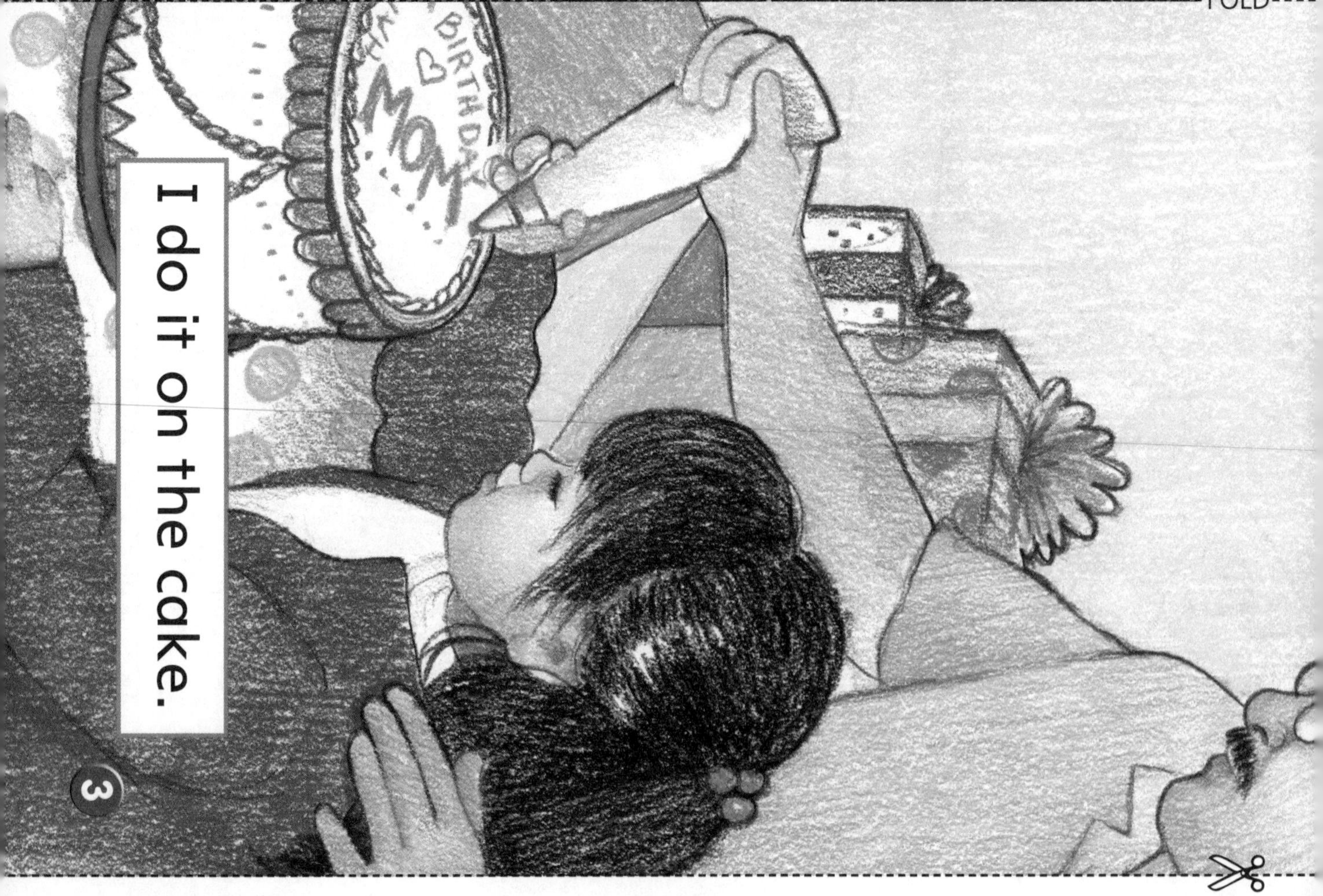

I do it on the cake.

3

Name ______________________________

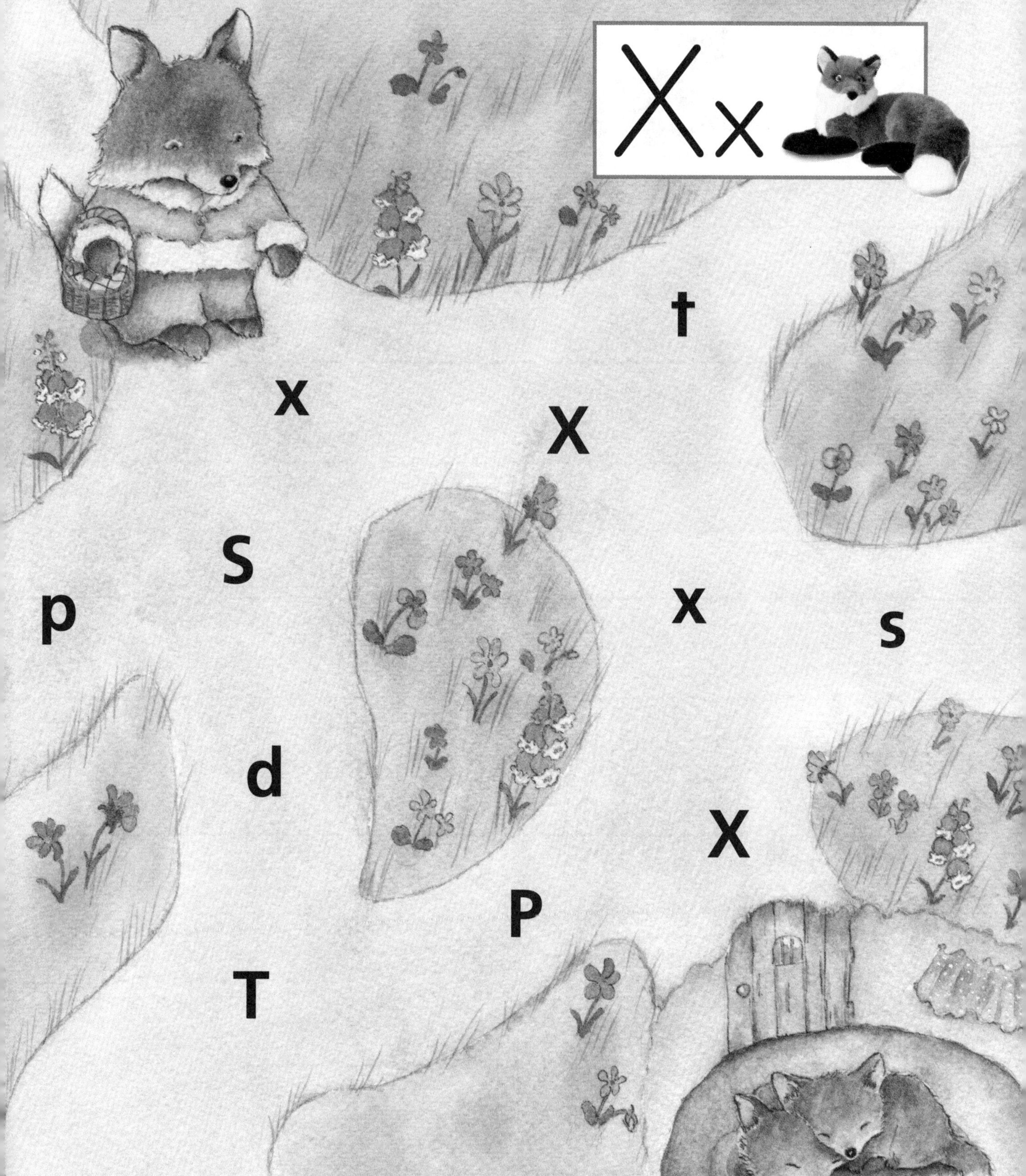

Directions: Have children identify the partner letters at the top of the page. Then, have children find and circle the alternating letters *X* and *x* to help the fox get to her den.

box

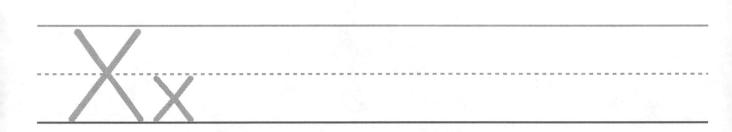

Directions: Have children trace the letters and print their own *X* and *x* on the lines. Then, have them identify the picture and complete the word.

HOME Invite your child to print *X* and *x*. Write words *fox in a box*, omitting the *x's*. Have your child complete the words and draw a picture.

Name ________________________________

Xx 

Directions: Help children identify the pictures. If a picture name ends with the sound of *x*, have children circle the picture.

Xx

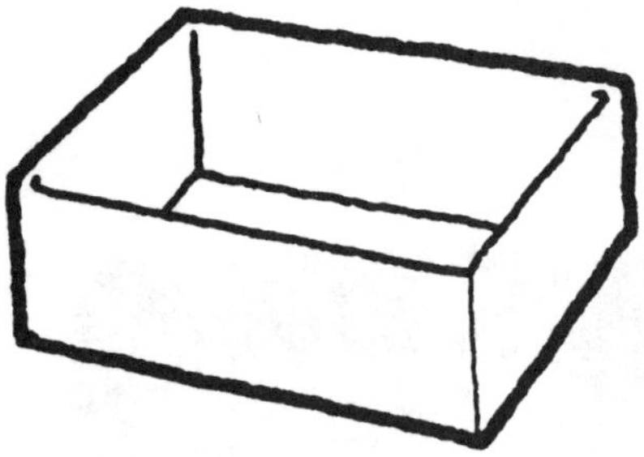

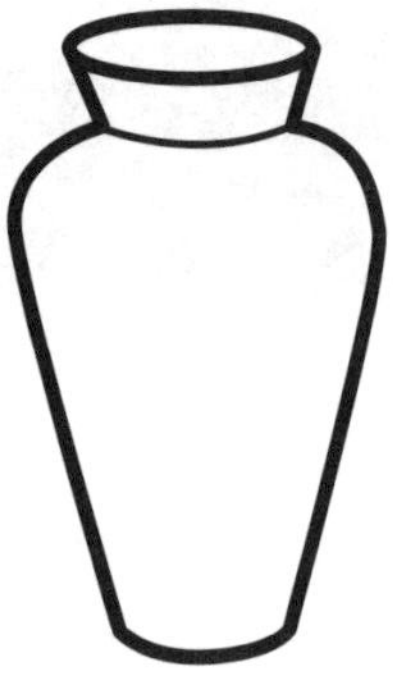

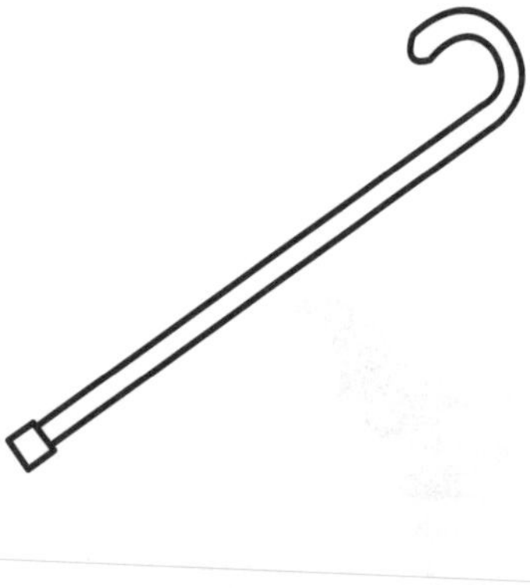

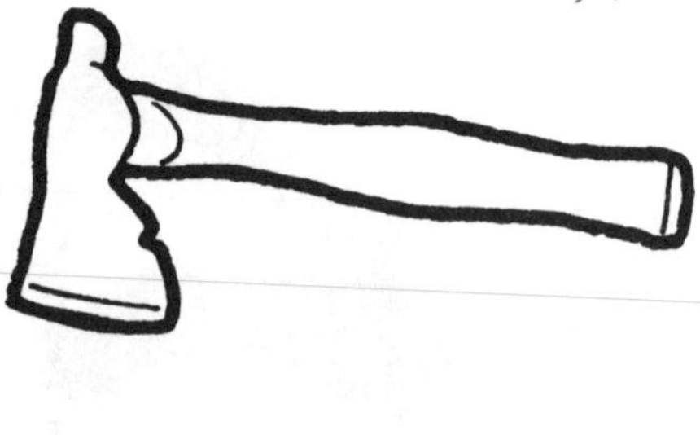

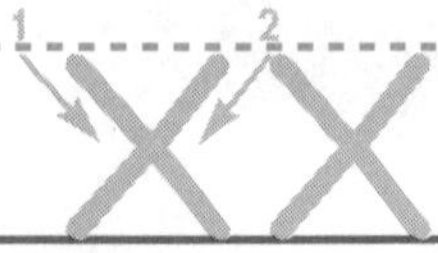

Directions: Ask children to color each picture whose name ends with the sound of *x* and draw a line from the picture to the fox. Then, have them practice printing the letter *x* on the line at the bottom of the page.

HOME

Print the words *mix*, *box*, *ax*, on paper. Have your child point to the letter *x* in each word, then write *Xx* on the paper.

Name ______________________________

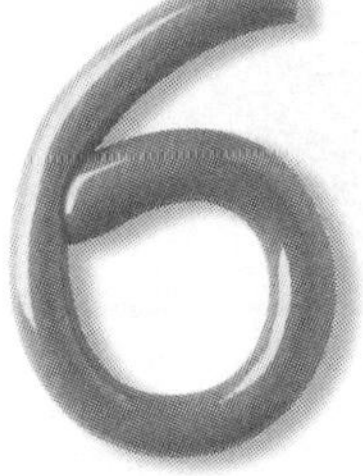

Directions: Help children name the pictures. If a picture name ends with the sound of *x*, have children print *Xx* on the line.

Xx

fo

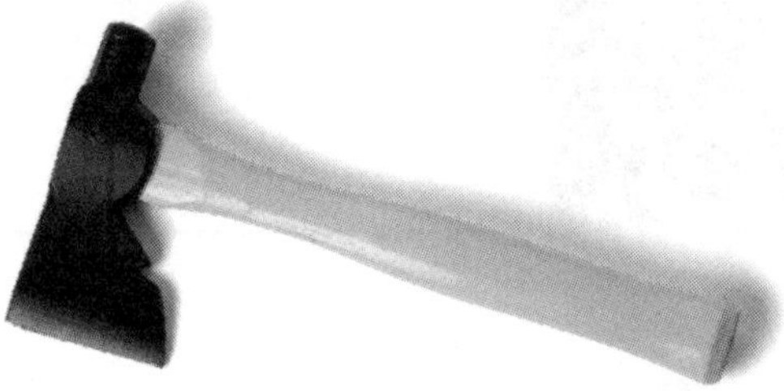

ax

si

bo

Directions: Have children name each picture and trace or print the letter *x* to complete each word. Point to and say each word as children say it with you.

HOME Give a clue about a dictionary word, such as *This word is a number*. Have your child point to and say the word.

Name ______________________________

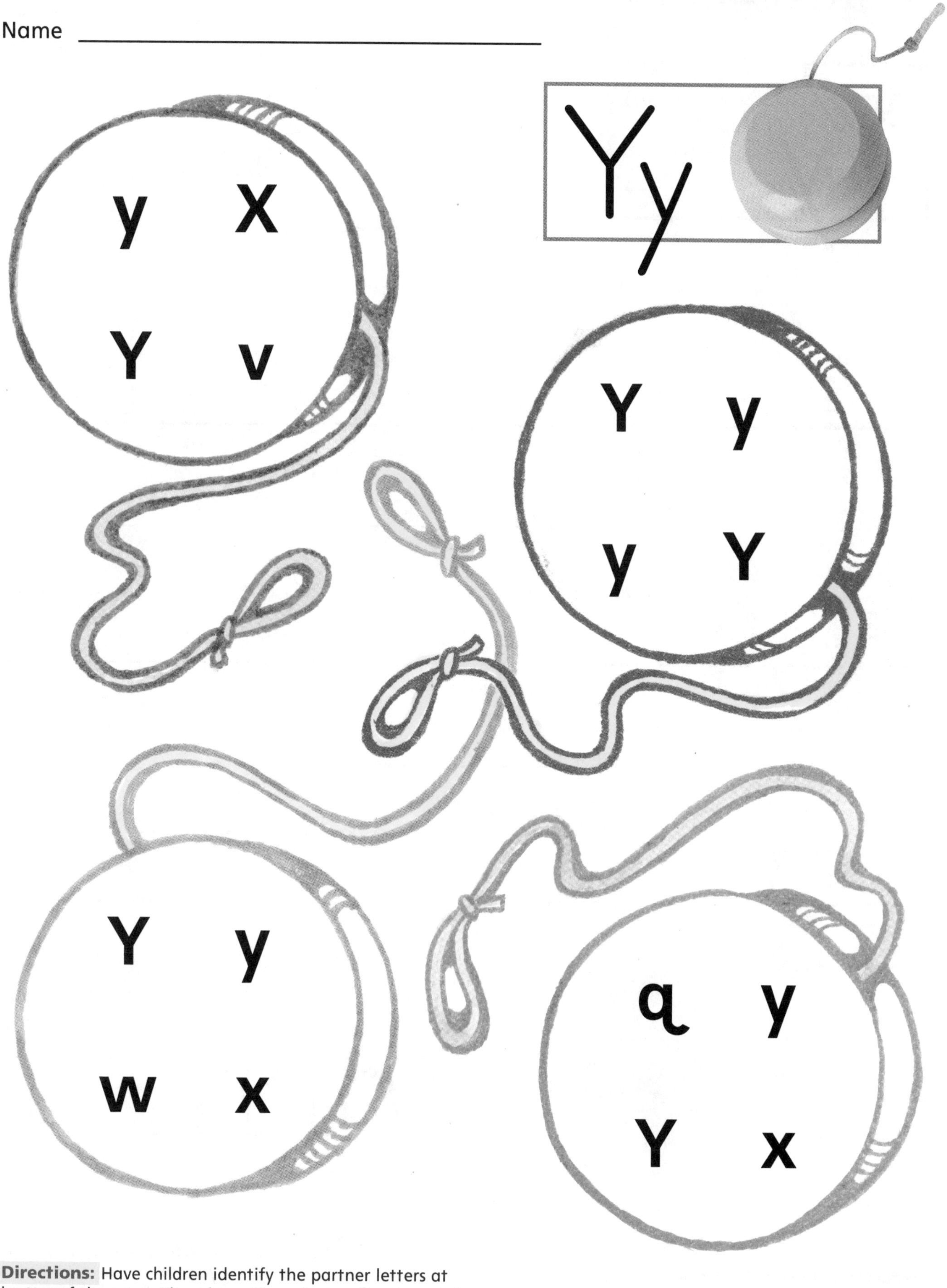

Directions: Have children identify the partner letters at the top of the page. Then, have them draw a line to match the partner letters *Y* and *y* on each yo-yo. Ask them to color the yo-yo that shows only the letters *Y* and *y*.

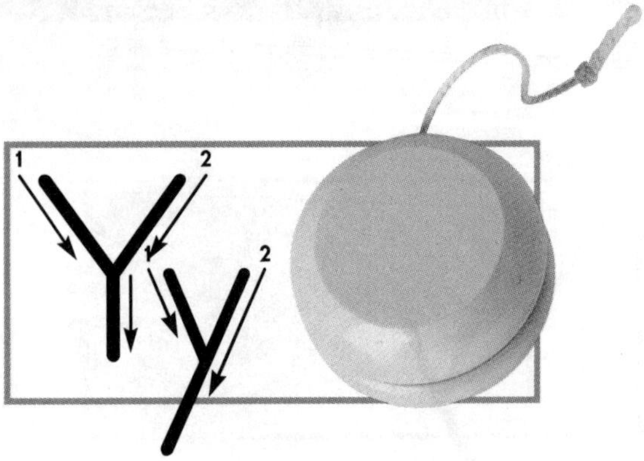

Y Y

y y

Y y

yarn

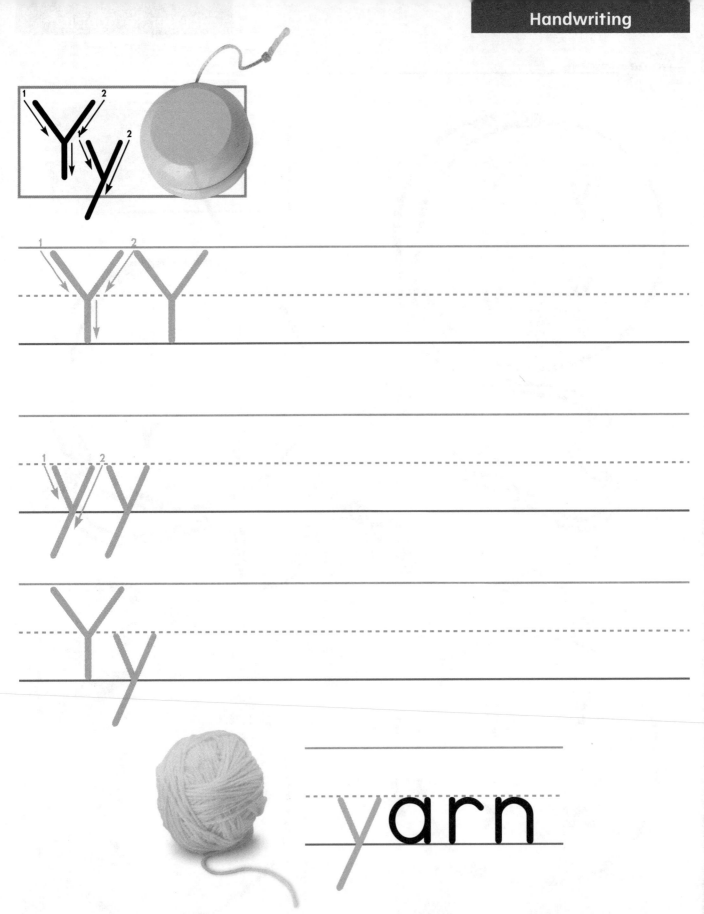

Directions: Have children trace the letters and print their own *Y* and *y* on the lines. Then, have them identify the picture and complete the word.

HOME Write the letters *Q*, *P*, *x*, *Y*, *v*, *g*, *R*, *y*, *w*. Have your child find and trace *Y* and *y* using a yellow crayon, then print *Y* and *y* on their own.

Name ____________________________

Yy 

Directions: Help children identify the pictures. If a picture name begins with the sound of *y*, have children circle the picture.

Yy

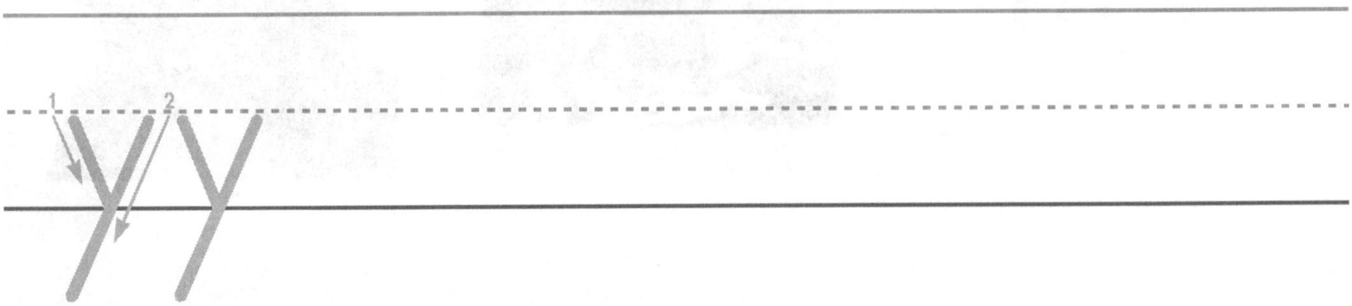

Directions: Help children identify the pictures, then have them use a yellow crayon to color each puzzle piece with a picture whose name begins with *y*. Ask children to name the letter that appears, then practice printing the letter *y*.

HOME Say words such as *yellow*, *vine*, *yarn*, *six*, *yo-yo*, *queen*, *yard*. Ask your child to say "yes" for each word that begins with *y*.

Name ______________________________

Yy

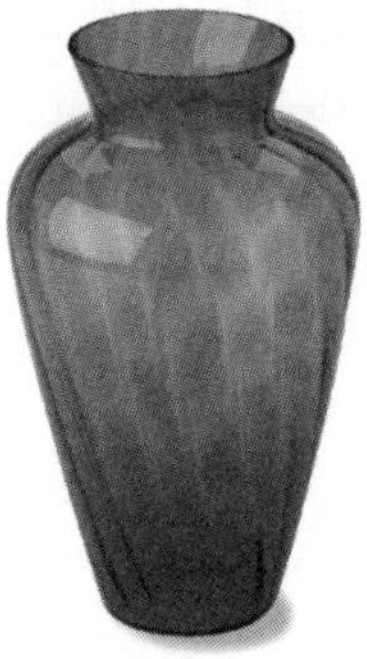

Directions: Help children name the pictures. If a picture name begins with the sound of *y*, have children print *Yy* on the line.

Yy

ogurt

yarn

awn

o-yo

Directions: Have children name each picture and trace or print the letter *y* to complete each word. Point to and say each word as children say it with you.

HOME Help your child make up silly sentences using words that begin with the *y* sound, such as *Yaks use yellow yo-yos.*

Name ______________________

Zz 

■ z	X	Y	Z
● Z	v	z	x
▲ z	Z	Y	W
★ Z	z	r	x

Directions: Have children identify the letter at the beginning of each row. Ask them to circle the letter in each row that is the partner letter.

ZZ

zz

Zz

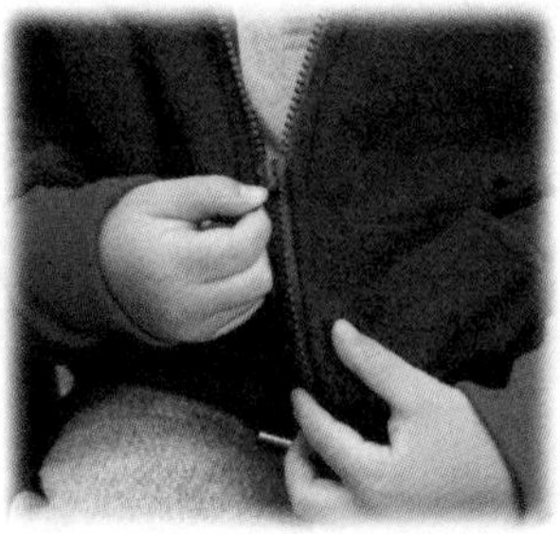

zipper

Directions: Have children trace the letters and print their own *Z* and *z* on the lines. Then, have them identify the picture and complete the word.

HOME

Help your child cut out a large paper *Z*. Invite your child to fill the paper letter by writing *Z* and *z* in a variety of colors.

Name ______________________________

Zz 

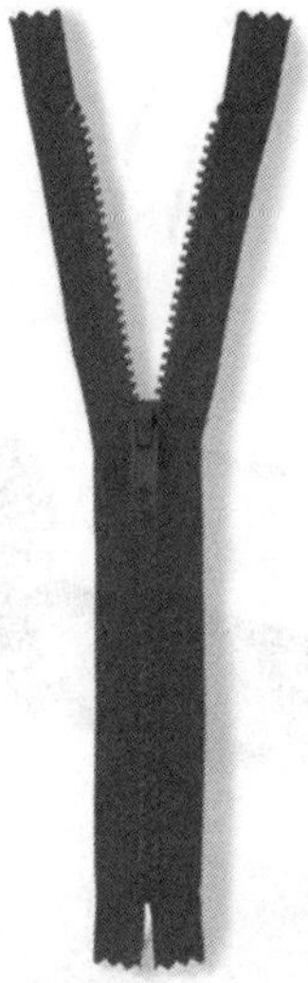

Directions: Help children identify the pictures. If a picture name begins with the sound of *z*, have children circle the picture.

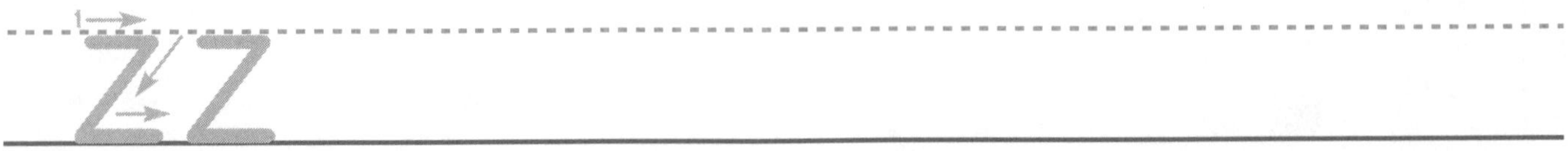

Directions: Help children name the pictures on each car. Have them color each car that has a picture name that begins with *z*. Then, have children practice printing the letter *z* on the line.

HOME Have your child print *z*, *p*, and *v*. As you say words that begin with these letters, have your child point to the letter.

Name ______________________________

Zz

Directions: Help children name the pictures. If a picture name begins with the sound of *z*, have children print *Zz* on the line.

Zz 

zebra

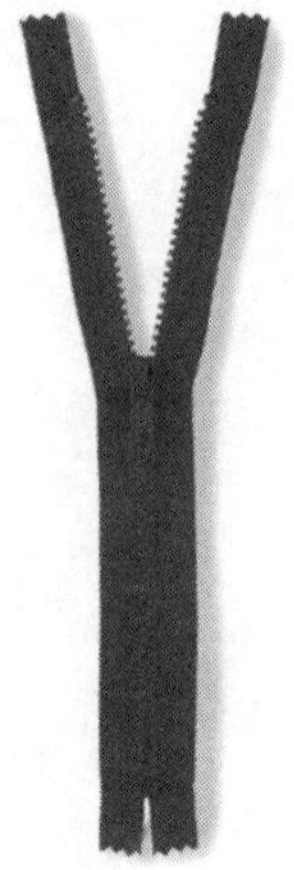

ipper

ero

oo

Directions: Have children name each picture and trace or print the letter *z* to complete each word. Point to and say each word as children say it with you.

HOME Help your child make up a sentence for each dictionary word, such as *I see zebras in the zoo.*

Name ______________________________

X

z
Y
x

y

Z
Y
x

Y

z
y
X

z

X
y
Z

Z

z
x
Y

x

Y
X
z

Directions: Have children draw a line to match the letter under the picture to its partner letter.

Xx

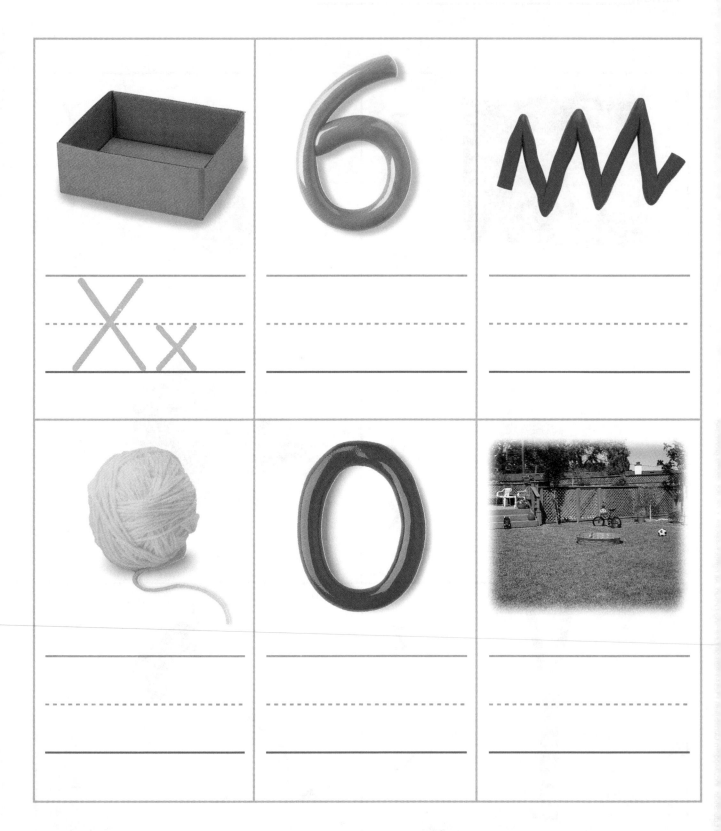

Directions: Have children name each picture. In the first box, have children trace the partner letters for the ending sound. In the other boxes, have children write the letters for the beginning or ending sound.

HOME Have your child name two pictures that begin or end with the same sound, then name other words that end with *x* or begin with *y* or *z*.

Name ______________________________

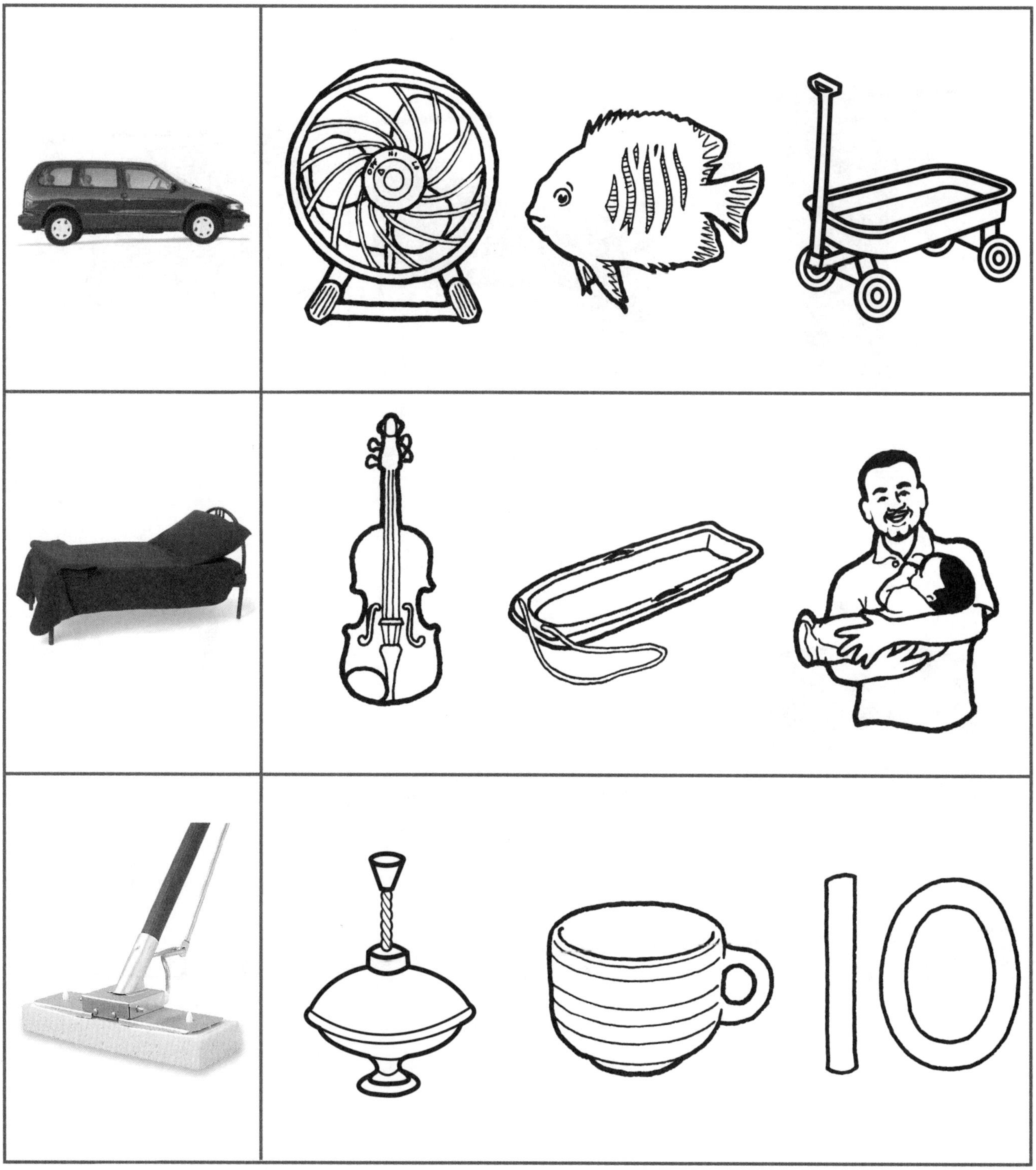

Directions: Say each picture name with children. Have children color the pictures in each row whose names end with the same sound as the picture in the box.

n d g

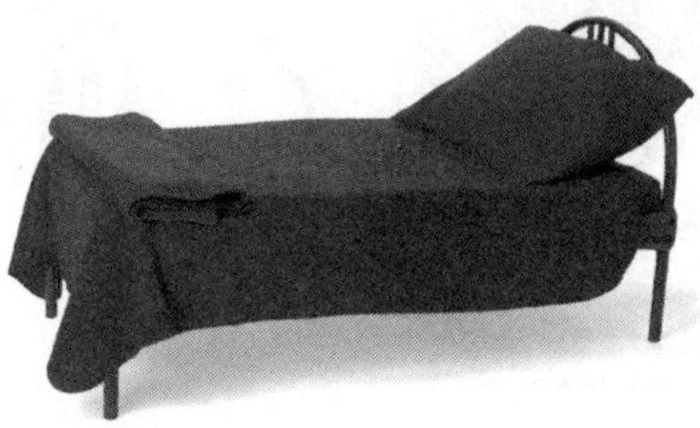

g n d

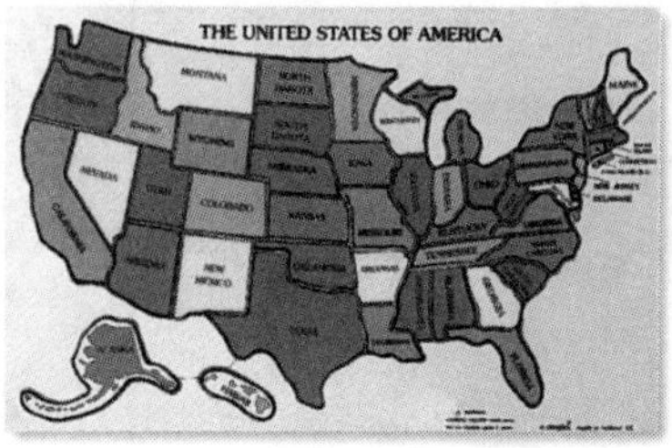

d p n

d n g

n d p

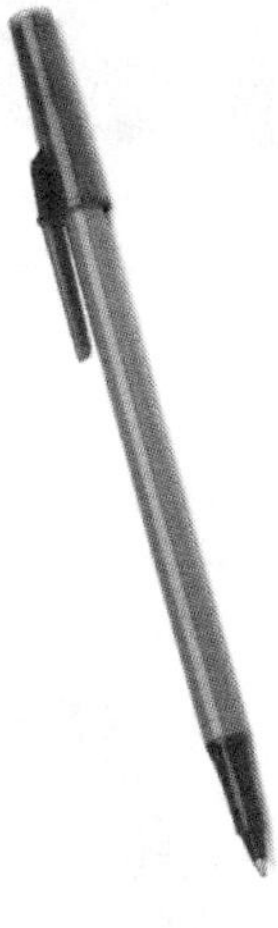

g d n

Directions: Say each picture name with children. Have children circle the letter that stands for the ending sound in each picture name.

HOME Write words such as *fan*, *bed*, and *cap*, omitting the final *n*, *d*, and *p*. Have your child print the letter to complete each word and draw a picture.

n v

q d

l p

w y

c n

r z

z p

q v

x z

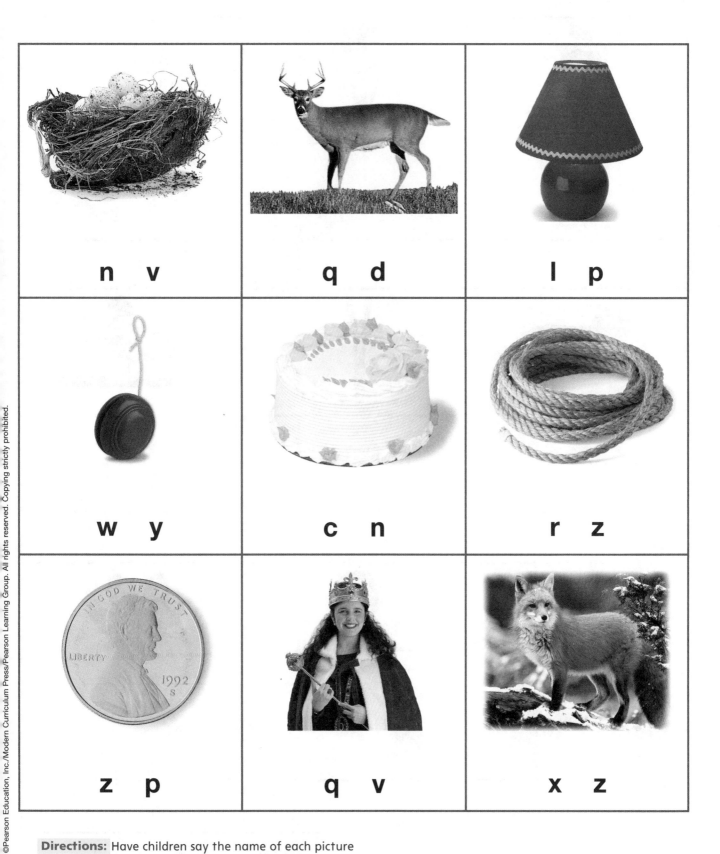

Directions: Have children say the name of each picture and, except for the last one, circle the letter that stands for the beginning sound. For the last picture, have children circle the letter that stands for the ending sound.

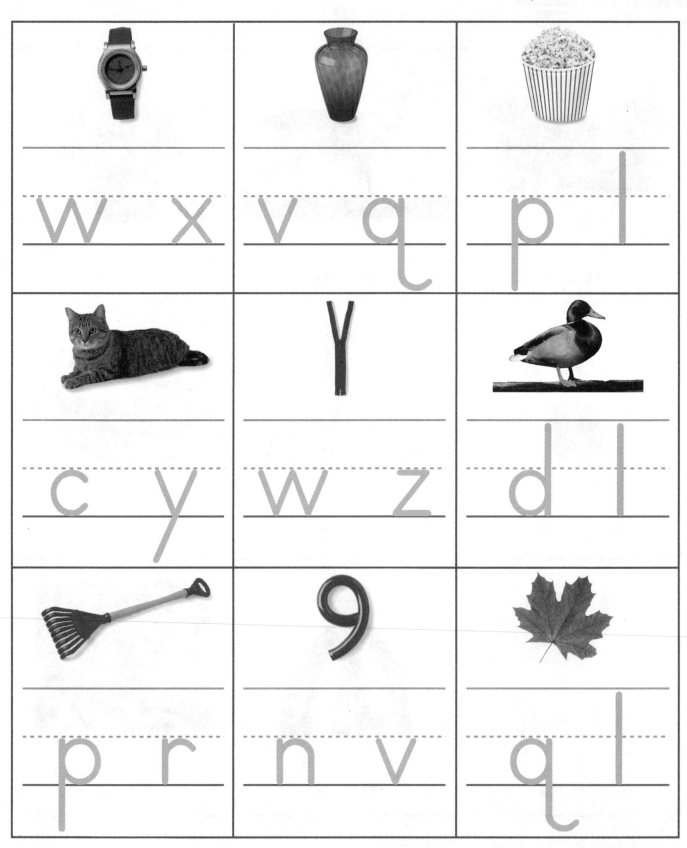

 w x	 v q	 p l
 c y	 w z	 d l
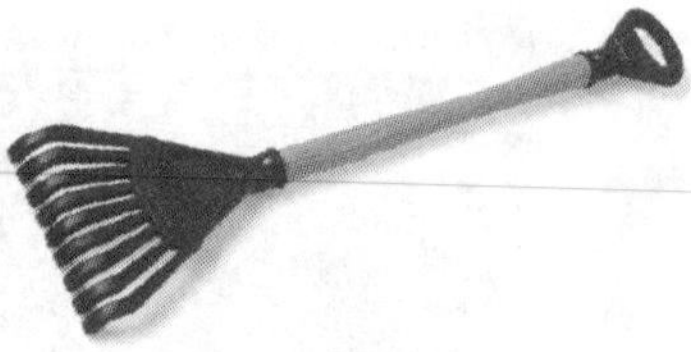 p r	 n v	 q l

Directions: Have children name the pictures, then trace the letter that stands for the beginning sound.

HOME Ask your child to name each picture, then say another word that begins with the same sound.

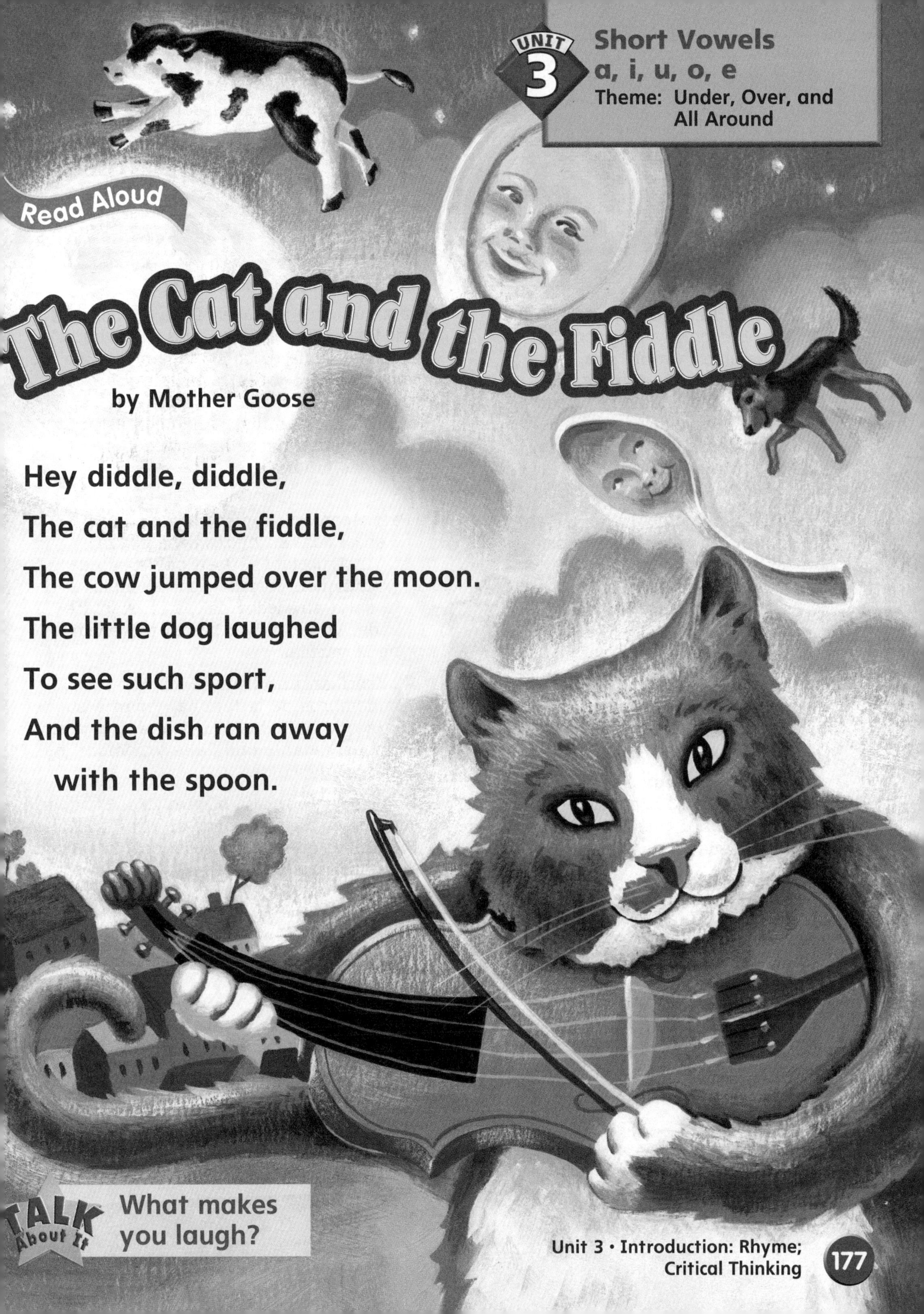

Read Aloud

The Cat and the Fiddle

by Mother Goose

Hey diddle, diddle,
The cat and the fiddle,
The cow jumped over the moon.
The little dog laughed
To see such sport,
And the dish ran away
with the spoon.

TALK About It
What makes you laugh?

HOME LETTER

Dear Family,

In this unit "Under, Over, and All Around," your child will learn the sounds the short vowels **a**, **e**, **i**, **o**, and **u** make at the beginning of words and in the middle of words. As your child develops an understanding of these sounds, you may wish to try these activities.

▶ Play a game outdoors for which your child must follow directions. Use position words, such as hop around the yard; sit under the tree; jump over the stick.

▶ Write a list of family members' names. Ask your child to find the letters **a**, **e**, **i**, **o**, and **u**. Then have your child find and name the capital letters.

▶ Read aloud to your child. Look for stories about outdoor adventures. Ask if these books are available in your local library.

He Saves the Day
by Marsha Hayles

Hello Toes! Hello Feet!
by Ann Whitford Paul

Sincerely,

____

jump

hop

Estimada familia:

En esta unidad, titulada "Debajo, encima y alrededor" ("Under, Over, and All Around"), su hijo/a estudiará los sonidos breves de las vocales **a**, **e**, **i**, **o** y **u** al principio y a la mitad de palabras en inglés. A medida que su hijo/a se vaya familiarizando con estos sonidos, pueden hacer las siguientes actividades juntos.

▶ Participen en un juego al aire libre en el cual su hijo/a deba seguir instrucciones. Usen palabras que indiquen posición, por ejemplo: salta alrededor del patio; siéntate debajo del árbol; brinca por encima de la varilla.

▶ Escriban una lista de los nombres de miembros de la familia. Pidan a su hijo/a que halle las letras **a**, **e**, **i**, **o** y **u**. Después, pídanle que halle y nombre las letras mayúsculas.

▶ Lean en voz alta a su hijo/a. Busquen cuentos sobre aventuras al aire libre. Pregunten en su biblioteca local si tienen disponibles estos libros.

He Saves the Day
de Marsha Hayles

Hello Toes! Hello Feet!
de Ann Whitford Paul

Sinceramente,

____

Name ______________________________

Aa

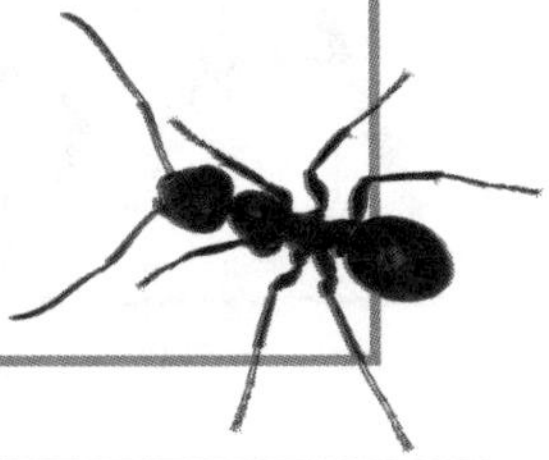

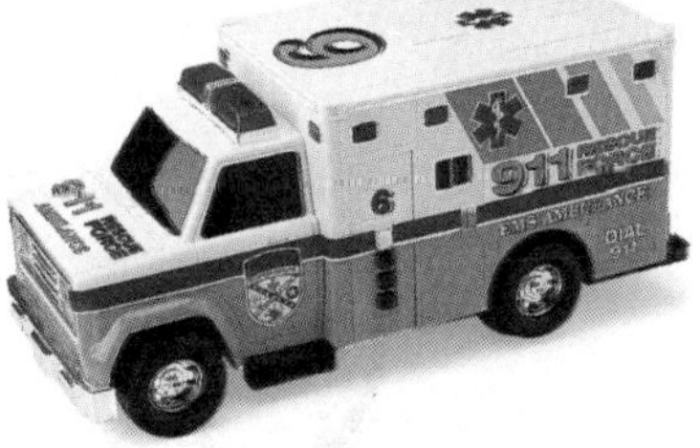

Directions: Invite children to name the pictures. Have them circle each picture whose name begins with the short *a* sound as in *ant*.

Aa

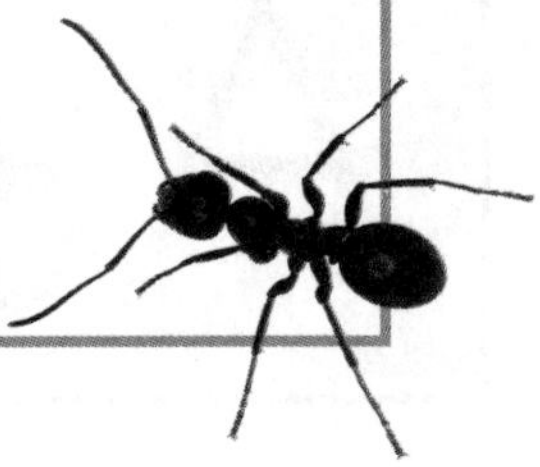

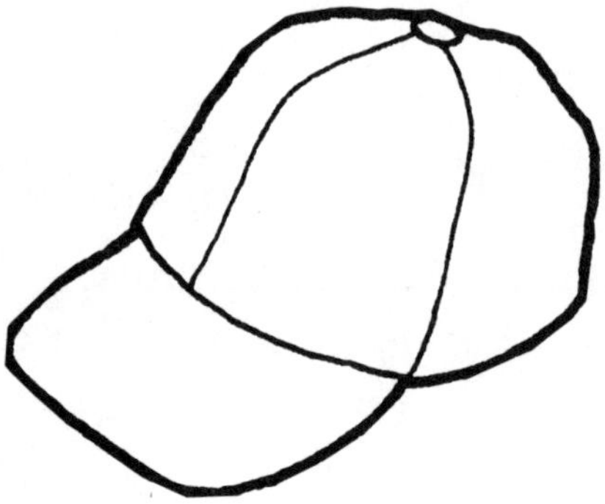

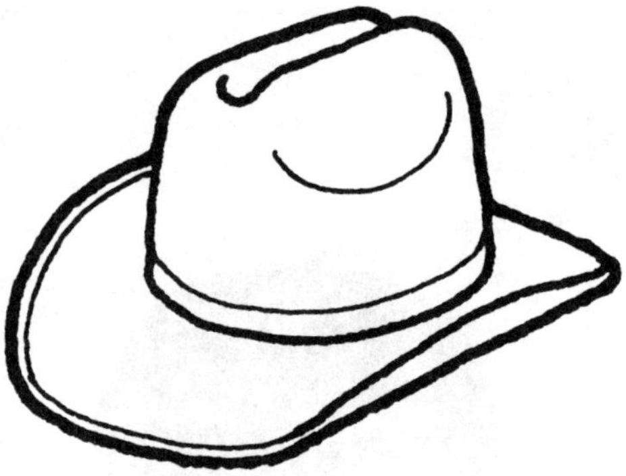

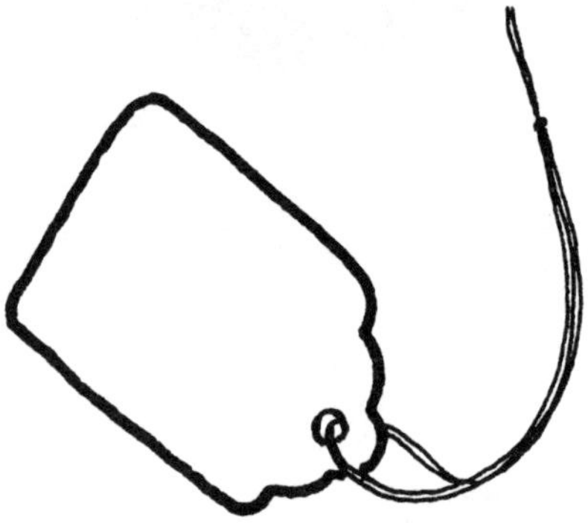

Directions: Help children to identify the bag in the center and to listen for the short vowel *a* sound in the middle of the word. Ask them to color each picture whose name has the medial sound of short *a* as in *bag*.

HOME Find magazine pictures, some with the short *a* sound. Have your child put the short *a* pictures in a bag.

Name ______________________

Aa

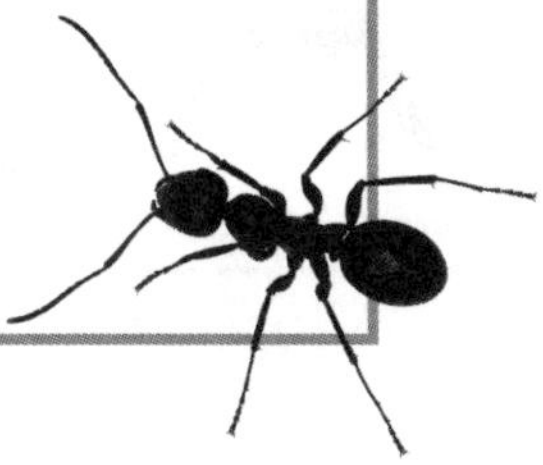

Aa

Directions: Have children say the name of each picture and write *Aa* if the name has the medial short vowel *a* sound. Then, invite them to say the picture names again and identify the two rhyming words.

Aa

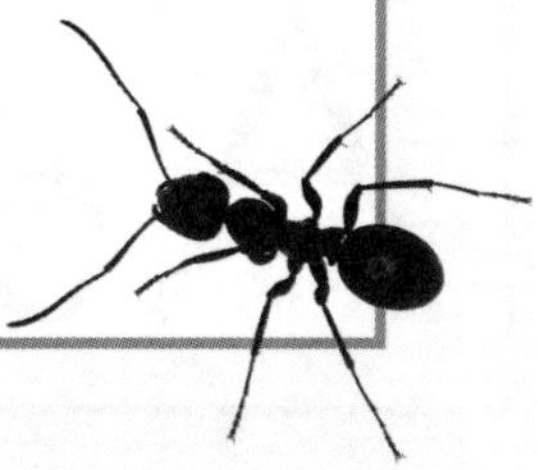

pple

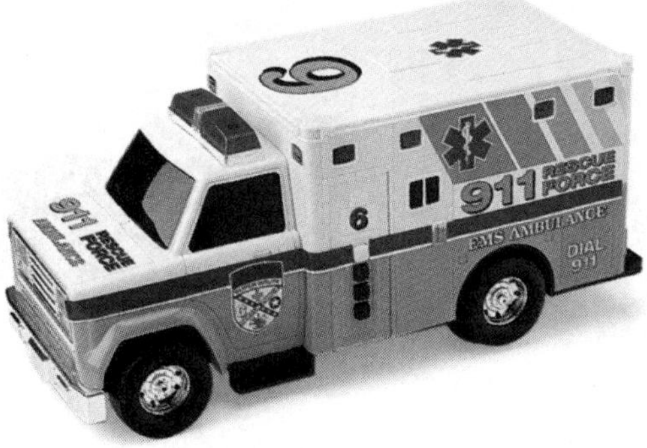

ambulance

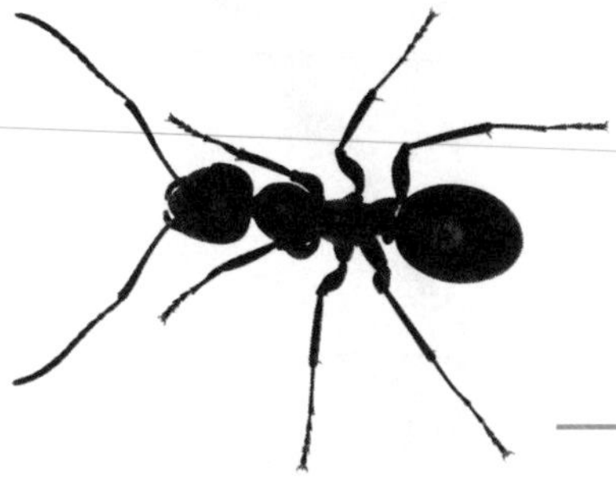

nt

x

Directions: Have children name each picture and write the letter *a* to complete each word. Point to and say each word as children say it with you.

HOME Write names of objects with short *a*, such as *cat*, omitting the *a*. Ask your child to write the *a*, then draw a picture.

Name ________________________________

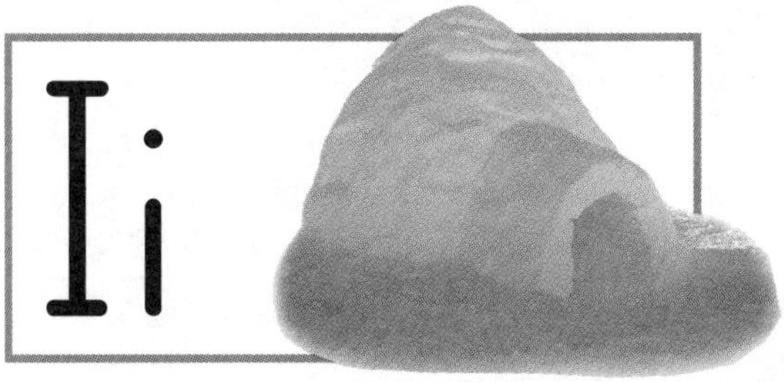

Directions: Have children identify the partner letters at the top of the page. Then, have children find the path with the alternating letters *I* and *i* and circle the letters to help the boy get to the igloo.

I I

i i

I i

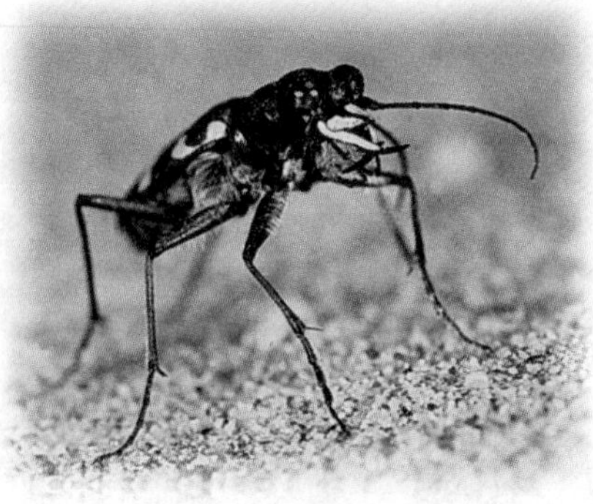

insect

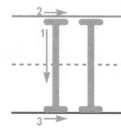

Directions: Have children trace the letters and print their own *I* and *i* on the lines. Then, have them identify the picture and complete the word.

HOME Have your child practice printing *I* and *i*, using markers with a variety of colors of ink.

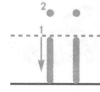

Name ______________________________

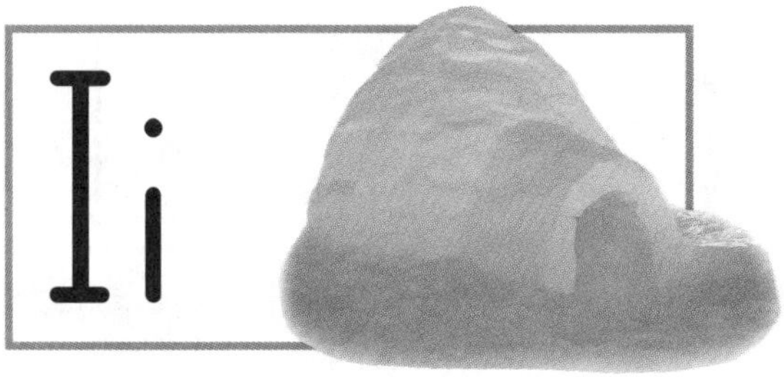

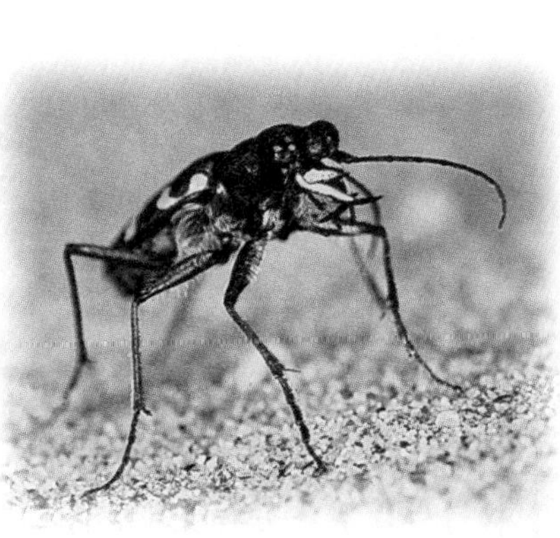

Directions: Help children identify the pictures. Have them circle each picture whose name begins with the short *i* sound.

Directions: Ask children to identify the picture on each fish on the page and listen for the short *i* sound in the middle of the word *fish*. Ask them to color each fish with a picture name that has the medial sound of short *i* as in *fish*.

HOME Say word pairs, such as *hat* and *lip*, *sun* and *pig*. Have your child repeat the word with short *i*.

Name ____________________

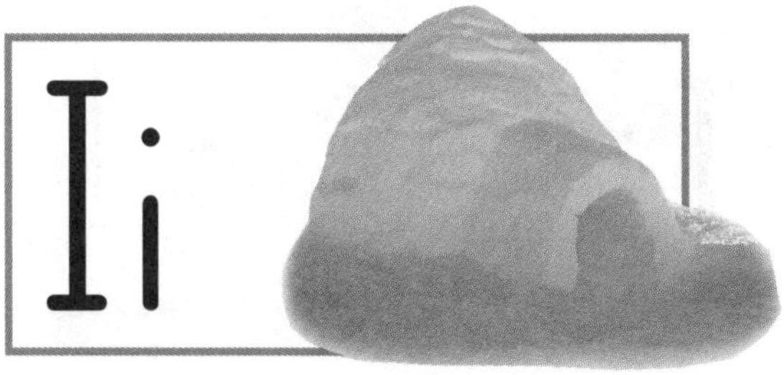

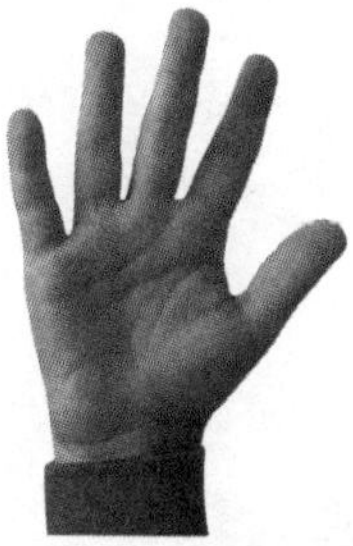

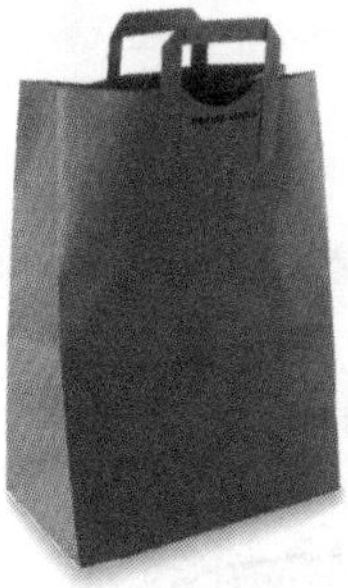

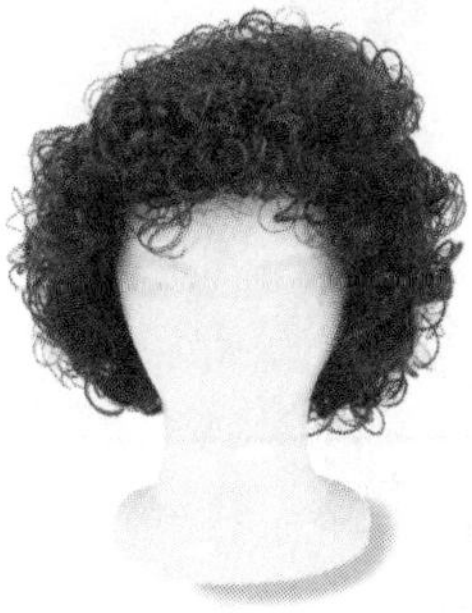

Directions: Have children say the name of each picture and print *Ii* if the picture name has the short vowel *i* sound. Have children say the picture names again and identify the two rhyming words (*pig*, *wig*).

Ii

igloo

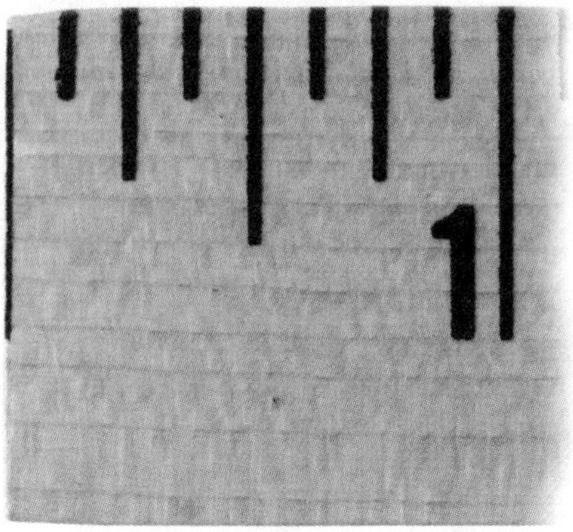

nch

guana

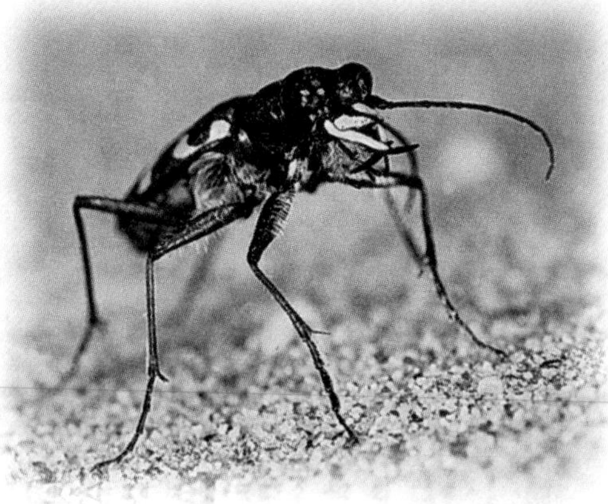

nsect

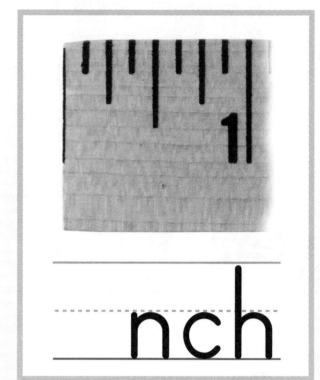

Directions: Have children name each picture and print the letter *i* to complete each word. Point to and say each word as children say it with you.

HOME Write words with short *i*, such as *pig* and *igloo*, omitting the *i*. Ask your child to write the *i* and draw a picture.

Name ______________________________

i a

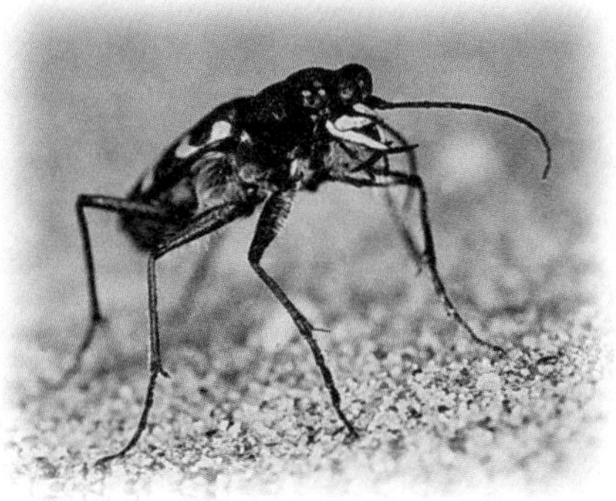

i a

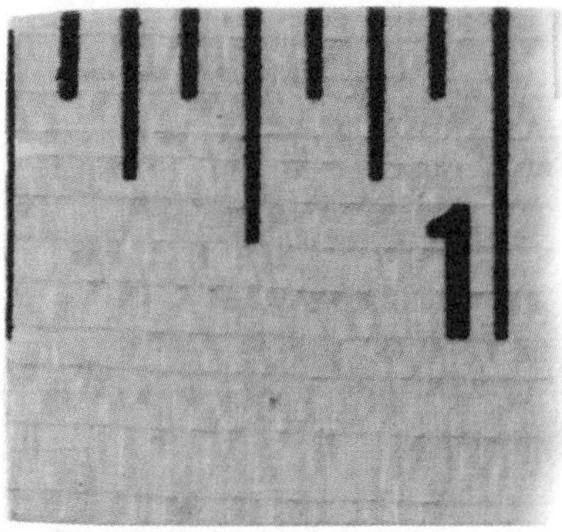

i a

i a

i a

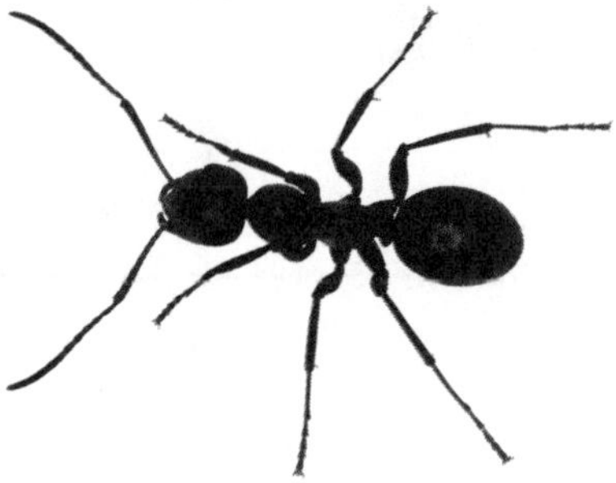

i a

Directions: Have children say the name of each picture, listen for the short vowel sound in the beginning of the word, and circle the letter that stands for that sound.

a

i

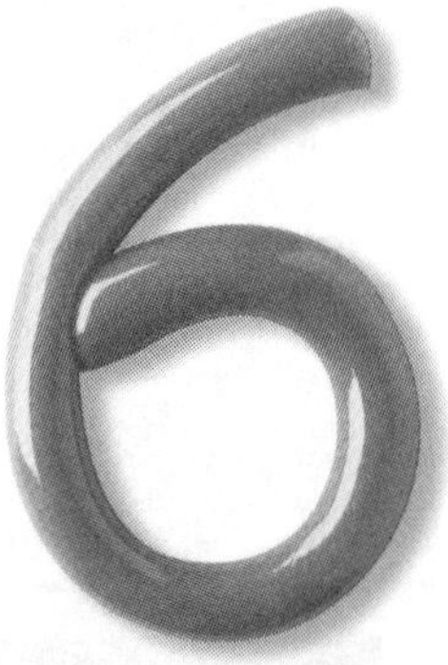

Directions: Have children say the name of each picture, listen for the short vowel sound in the middle of the word, and trace or write the letter *a* or *i* on the lines.

HOME

Write *a* and *i* on paper. Say *fan*, *map*, *bib*, *mitt*. Ask your child to point to the letter that makes the short vowel sound in each word.

Name ____________________

here	**we**
at	**look**

■ Look in here.

● Look at the .

▲ Now look at the .

★ How do we look?

Directions: Read the words in the box and have children repeat them. Have children say and trace the word in each sentence. Then, read the sentences with children.

here we
at look

■ Look here.

● Look at the .

▲ We like to look at .

★ Can we keep the ?

Directions: Help children to read each sentence. Then, have them trace each word to complete the sentence. Invite them to read the sentence again.

HOME Write the words from this lesson on a sheet of paper. Have your child say each word.

Look Here!

Name____________

Look here.

1

FOLD

We like our pets!

4

Directions: Read the story aloud, and discuss the pictures with the children.

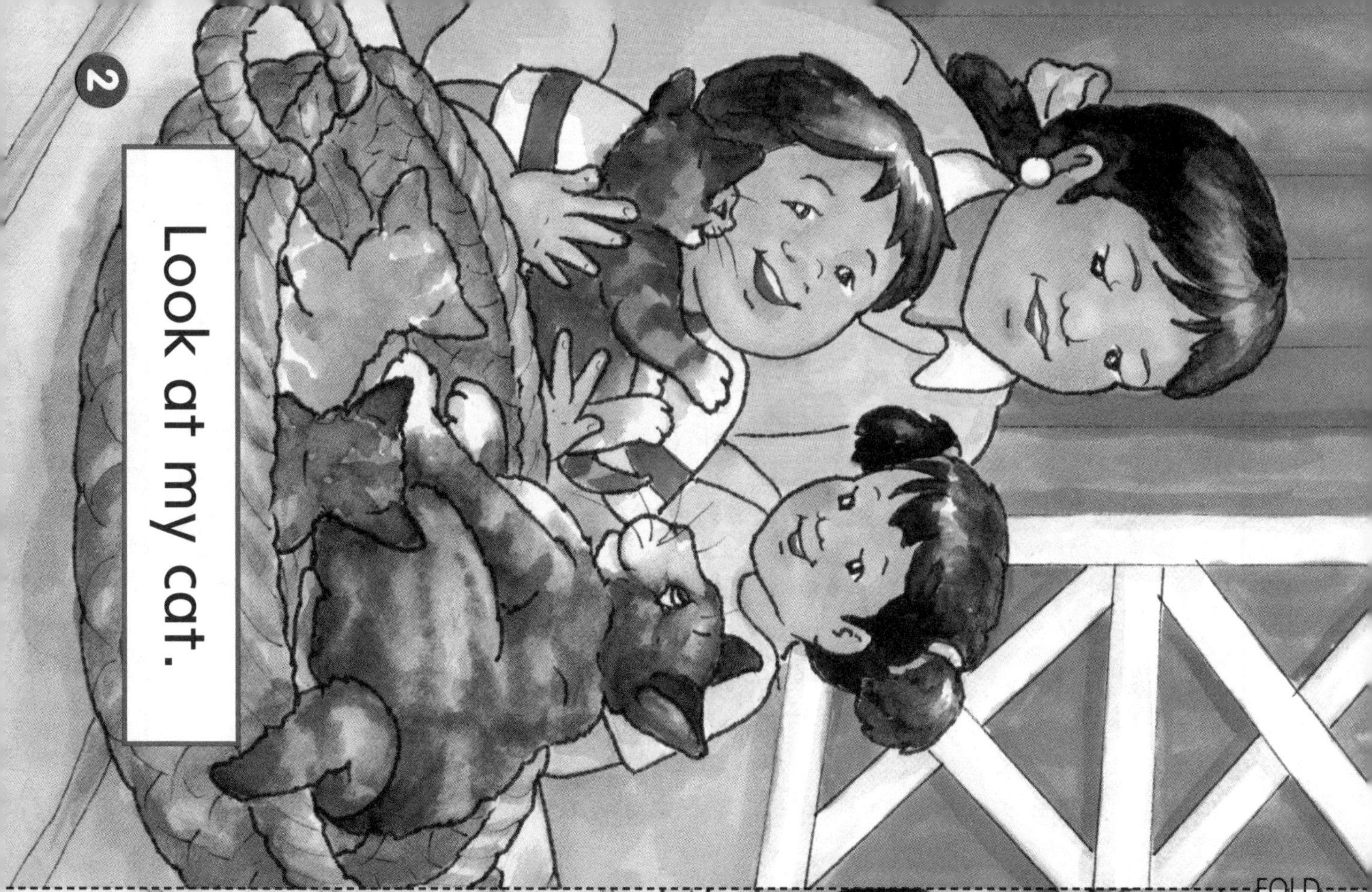
2
Look at my cat.

FOLD

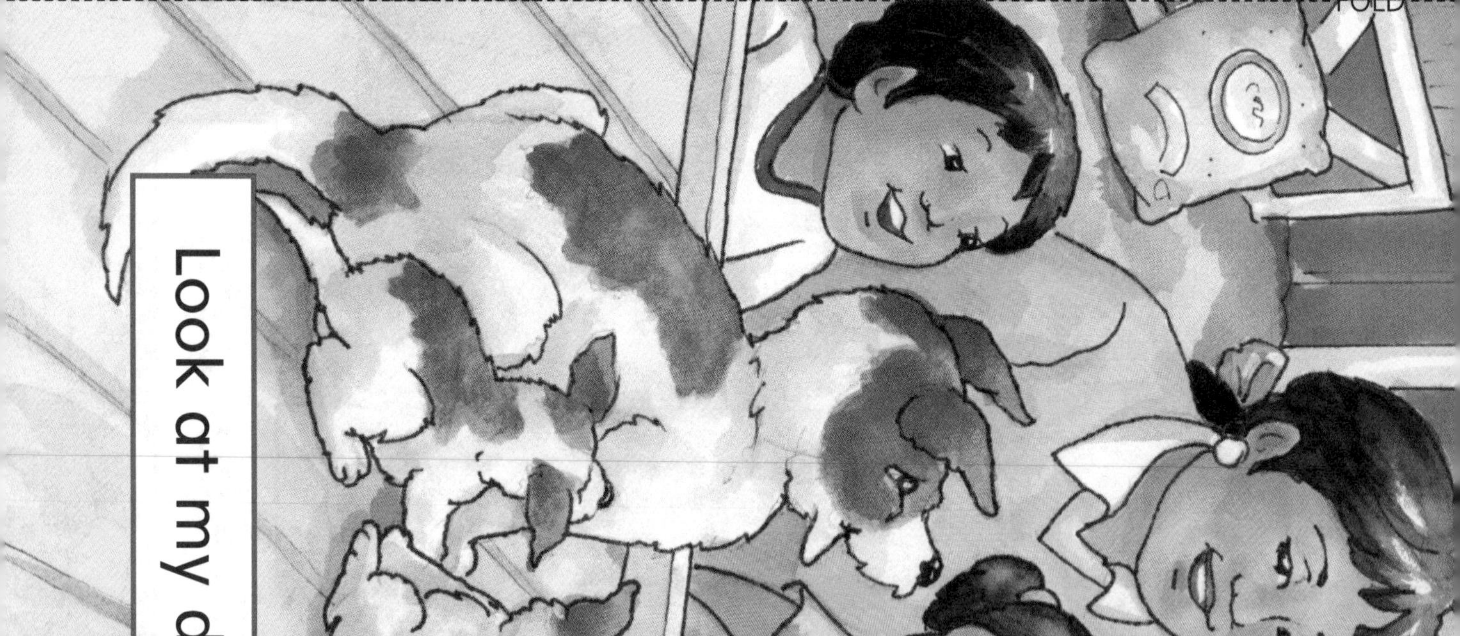
Look at my dog.
3

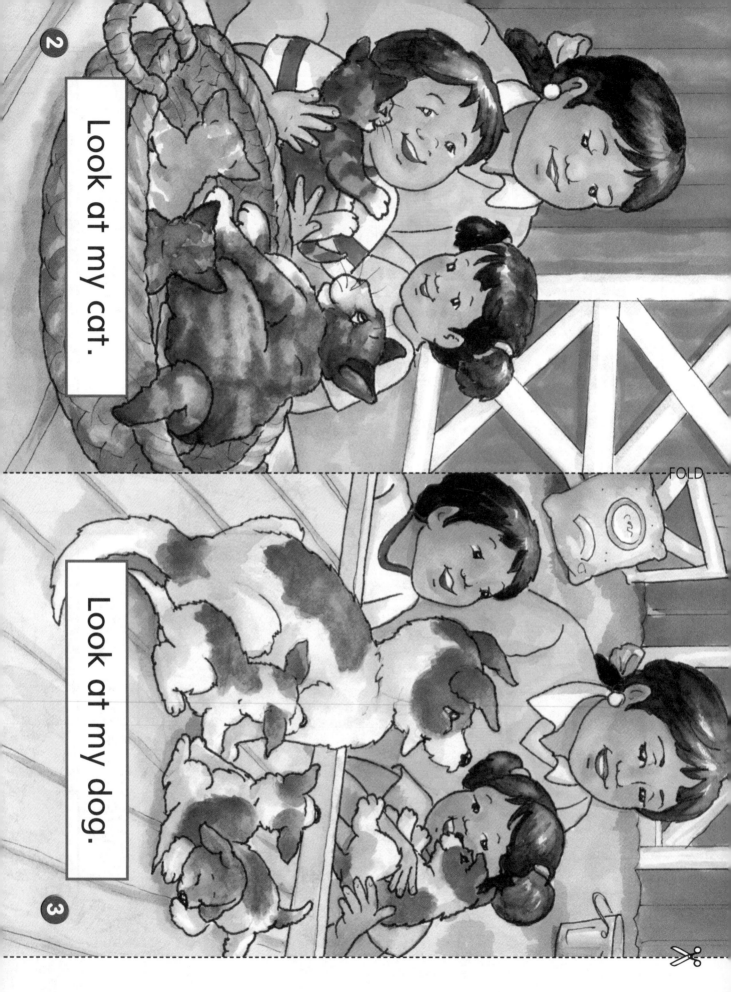

Name ________________________________

Directions: Have children identify the partner letters at the top of the page. Then have them look at each umbrella and draw a line to match *U* and *u*. Invite them to color the umbrella that shows only *U* and *u*.

U u

U U

u u

U u

under

Directions: Have children trace the letters and write their own *U* and *u* on the lines. Then, have them identify the picture and complete the word.

HOME Have your child practice writing *U* and *u*, then have them circle the best *U* and *u* they printed.

Name ______________________________

Uu

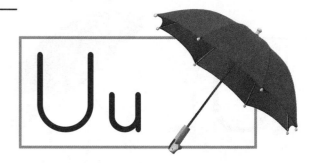

Directions: Help children identify the pictures. Have them circle each picture whose name begins with the short *u* sound.

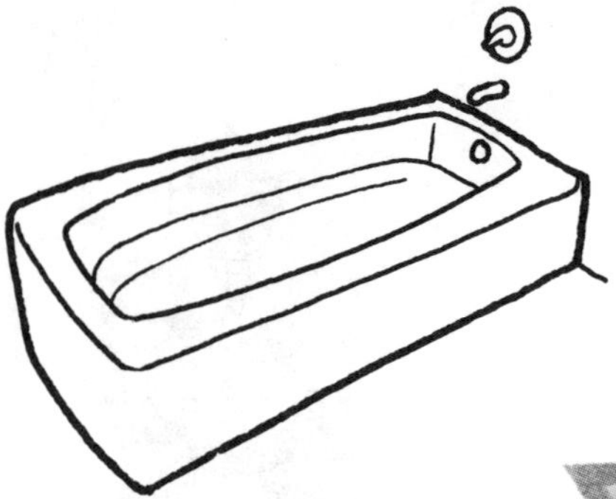

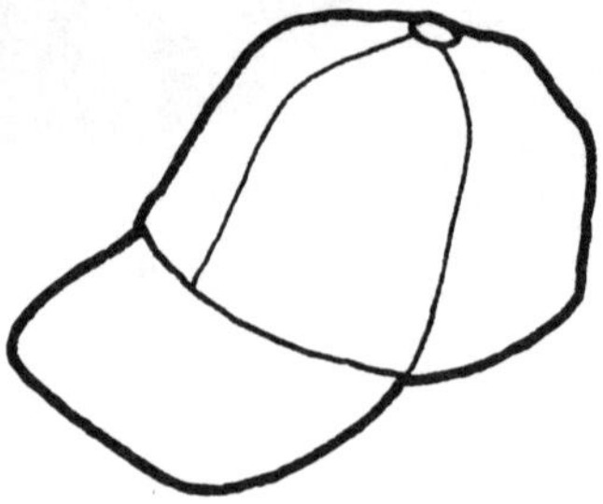

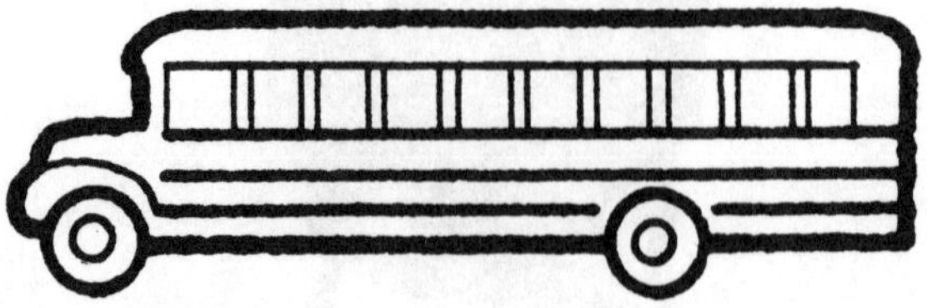

Directions: Ask children to identify the sun in the center and to listen for the short vowel *u* sound in the middle of the word. Ask them to color each picture whose name has the medial sound of short *u* as in *sun*.

HOME Say short u words *run*, *mug*, *luck*, *jump*, *gum*, and *cut*. Ask your child to repeat each word and try to say another word that rhymes with it.

Name ______________________________

Uu

Uu

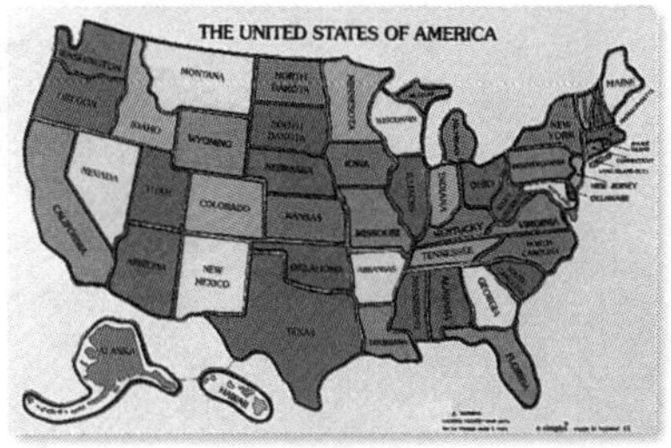

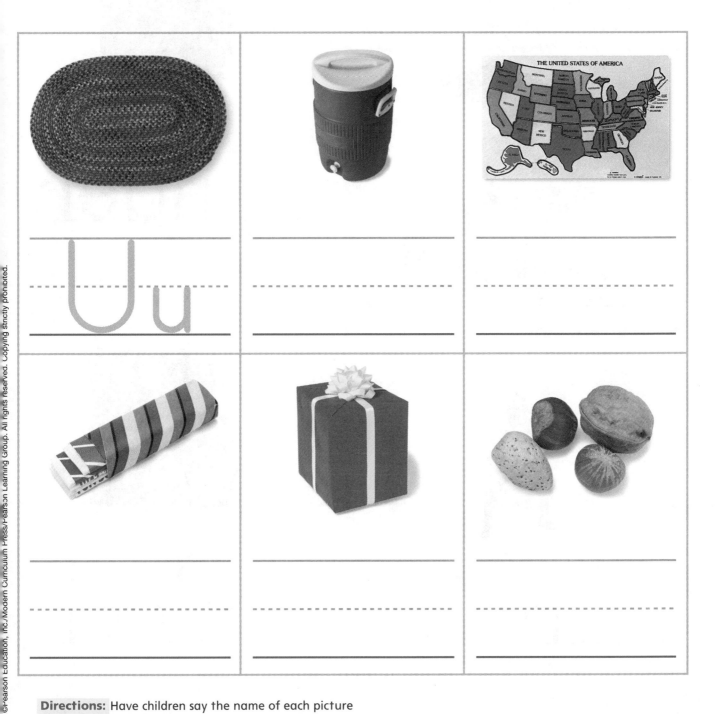

Directions: Have children say the name of each picture and write *Uu* if the picture name has the short vowel *u* sound. Have children say the picture names again and identify the two words that rhyme.

Uu

umbrella

nder

mpire

nlock

Directions: Have children name each picture and write the letter *u* to complete each word. Point to and say each word as children say it with you.

HOME Write words with short *u*, such as *duck* and *pup*, omitting the *u*. Ask your child to write the *u* and draw a picture.

Name ______________________________

Directions: Have children identify the partner letters at the top of the page. Then, have children follow the alternating letters *O* and *o* and draw a line connecting the letters to show the path the octopus takes to get to its cave.

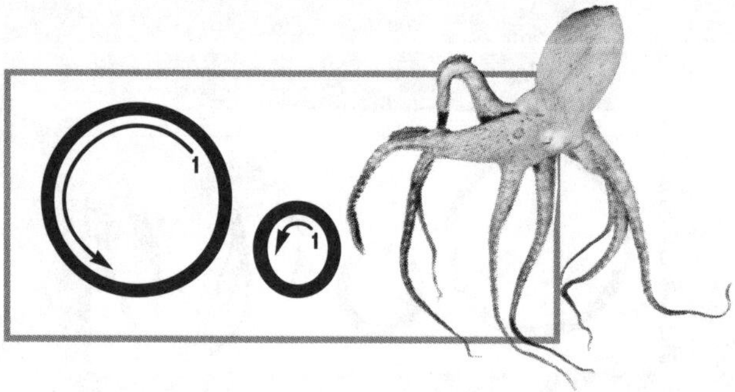

ox

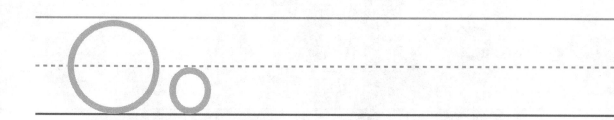

Directions: Have children trace the letters and write their own *O* and *o* on the lines. Then, have them identify the picture and complete the word.

HOME Have your child practice writing *O* and *o*, then have them look for letters *O* and *o* in books they have.

Name ______________________________

Oo

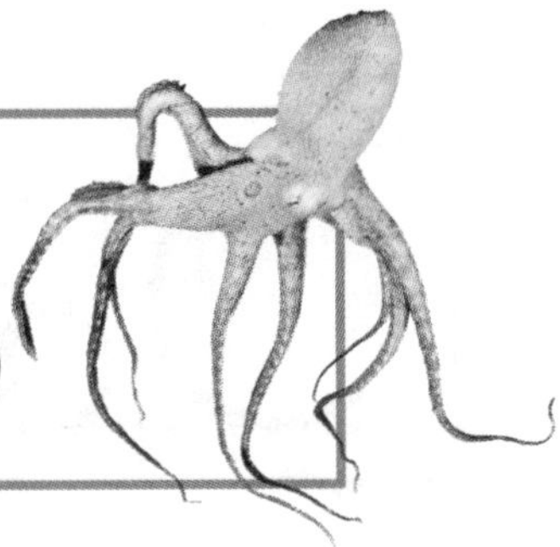

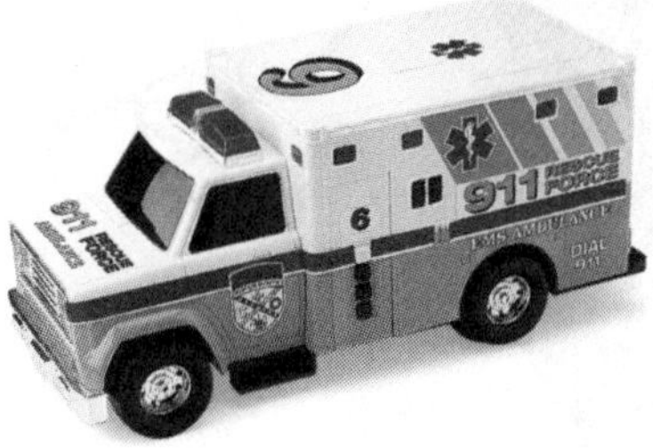

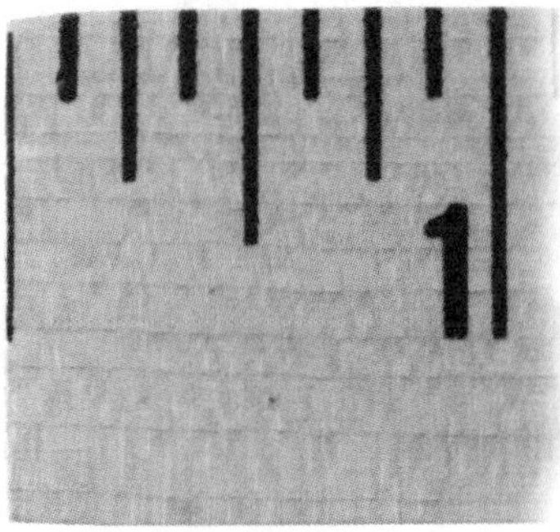

Directions: Help children identify the pictures. Have them circle each picture whose name begins with the short *o* sound.

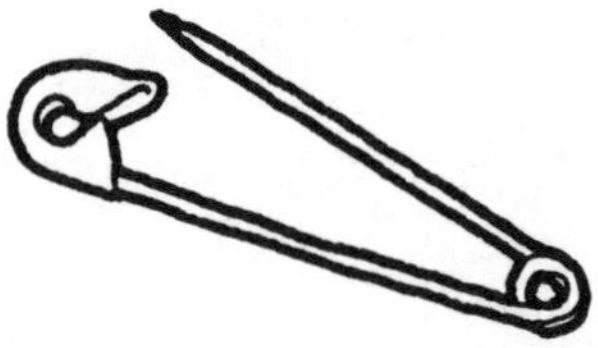

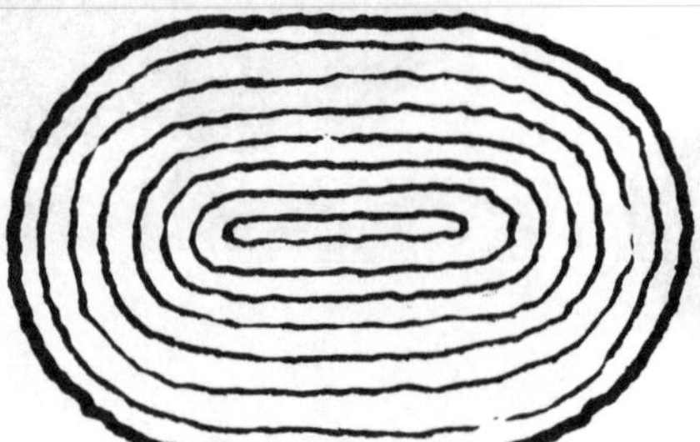

Directions: Identify the fox and box in the center and ask children to listen for the short vowel *o* sound in the middle. Have them color each picture whose name has the medial sound of short *o*, as in *fox* and *box*.

Find pictures, some with the short *o* sound. Have your child put the short *o* pictures in a box labeled *o*.

Name ______________________

O o

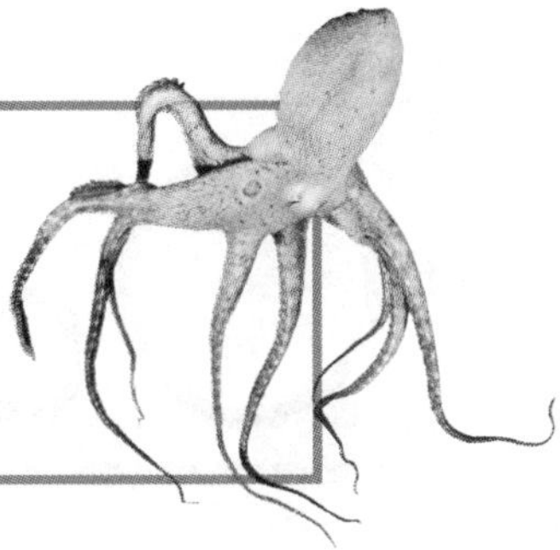

O o

Directions: Have children say the name of each picture and write *o* if the picture name has the short vowel *o* sound. Have children say the picture names again and identify the two rhyming words.

Oo

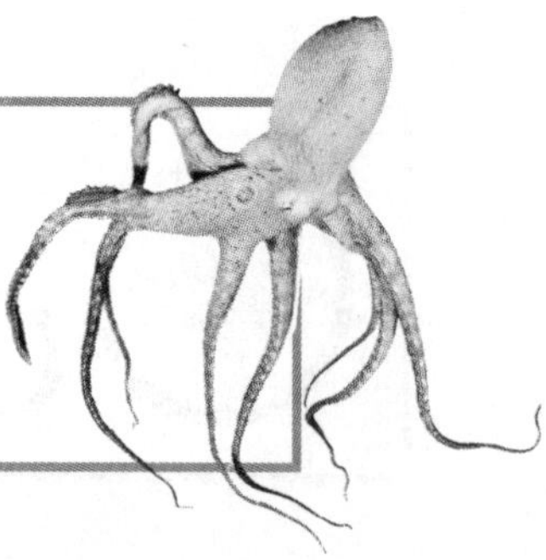

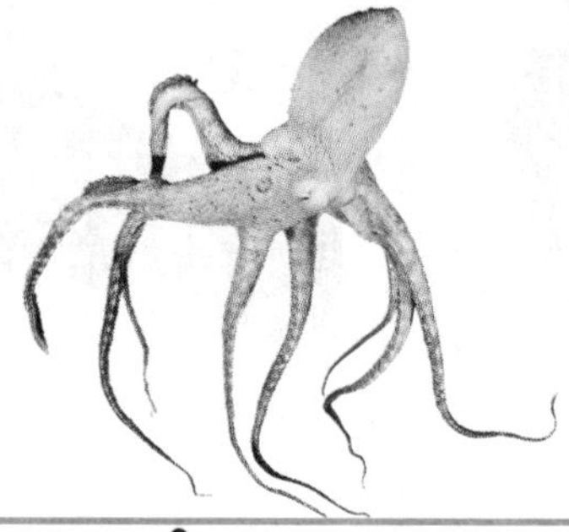

octopus

strich

tter

x

Directions: Have children name each picture and write the letter *o* to complete each word. Point to and say each word as children say it with you.

HOME Write animal names with short *o*, such as *frog* and *fox*, omitting the *o*. Ask your child to write the *o* and draw a picture.

Name ______________________________

Ee

■ e	A	E	V
● E	e	c	i
▲ e	F	T	E
★ E	o	e	s

Directions: Have children identify the letter at the beginning of each row. Ask them to circle the letter in each row that is the partner letter.

E E

e e

E e

elephant

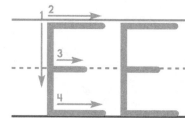

Directions: Have children trace the letters and write their own *E* and *e* on the lines. Then, have them identify the picture and complete the word.

HOME Have your child practice writing *U* and *u*, and then have them circle the best *U* and *u* they printed.

Name ______________________________

Ee

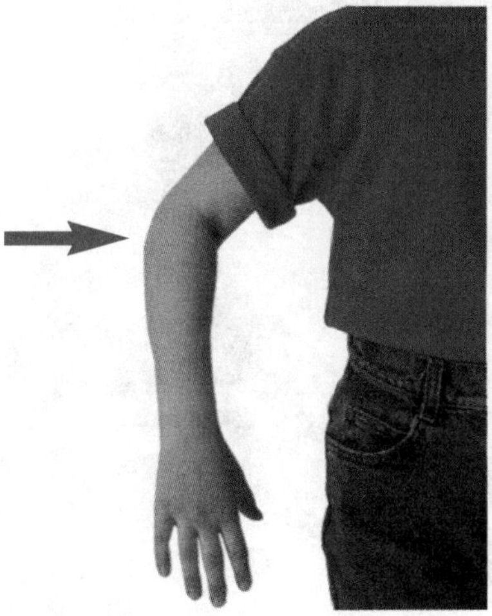

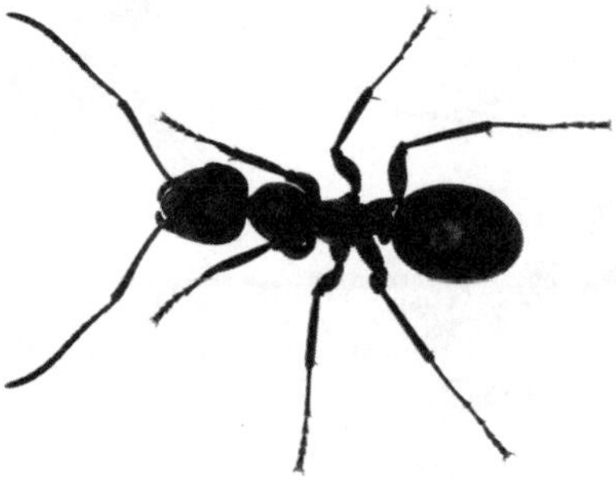

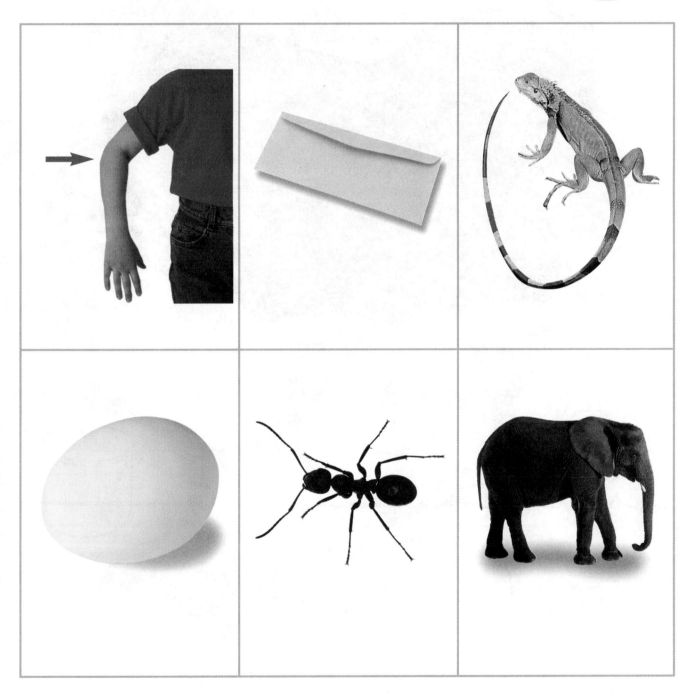

Directions: Help children identify the pictures. Have them circle each picture whose name begins with the short *e* sound.

Ee

Directions: Help children to identify the hen in her nest and to listen for the short e sound in the middle of the words. Ask them to color each egg with a picture whose name has the medial sound of short e as in *hen* and *nest*.

HOME Say the words *fed*, *west*, *pen*, *test*, *Deb*, *Ted*, *den* and ask your child to point to the *egg* with a picture name that rhymes.

Name ______________________________

Ee

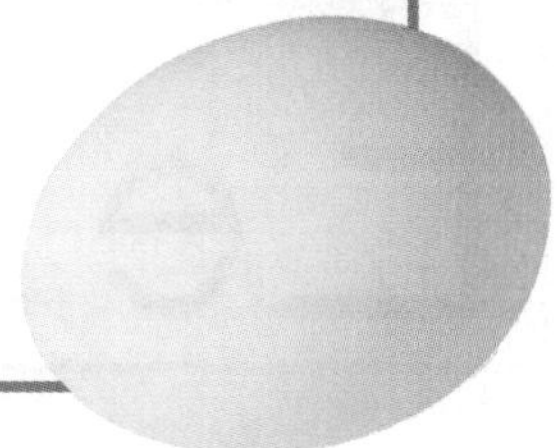

Ee

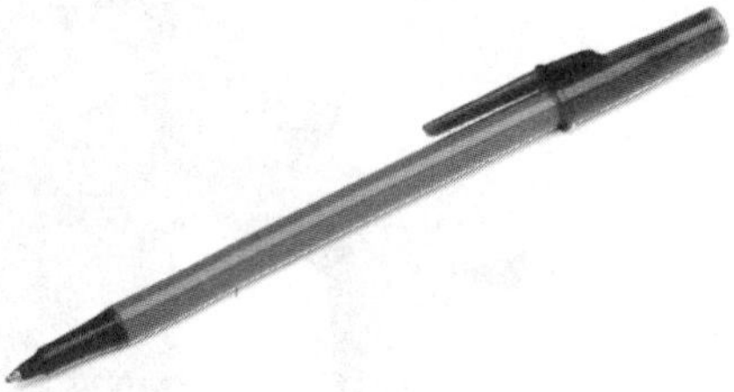

Directions: Have children say the name of each picture and write *Ee* if the picture name has the short vowel e sound. Have children say the picture names again and identify the two rhyming words.

Ee

egg

lephant

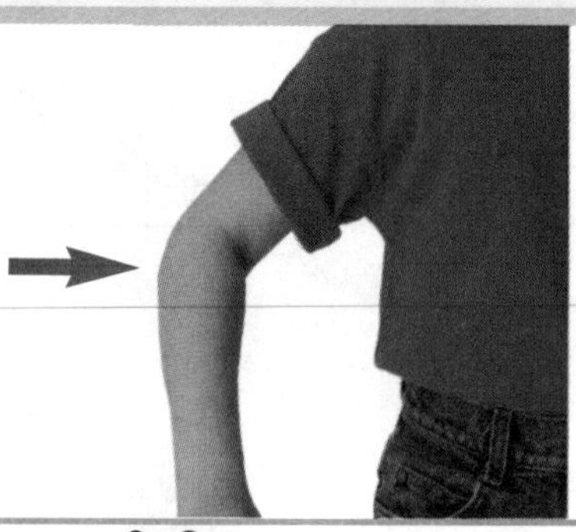

lbow

nvelope

Directions: Have children name each picture and write the letter e to complete each word. Point to and say each word as children say it with you.

HOME Write phrases with short e words, such as *ten hens* and *red bed*, omitting the *e's*. Ask your child to write the e and draw a picture.

Name ______________________________

u o

o e

u e

e o

u o

u e

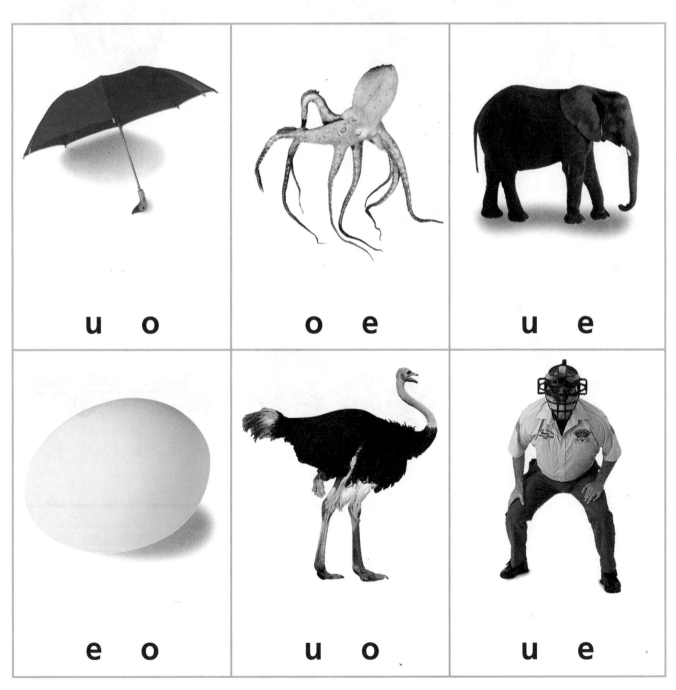

Directions: Have children say the name of each picture, listen for the short vowel sound in the beginning of the word, and circle the letter that stands for that sound.

Uu

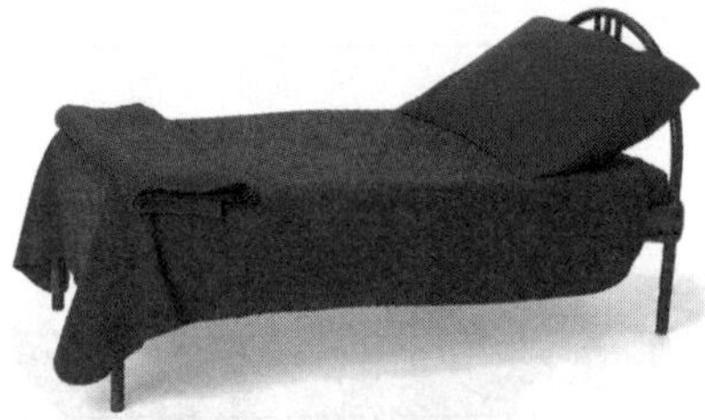

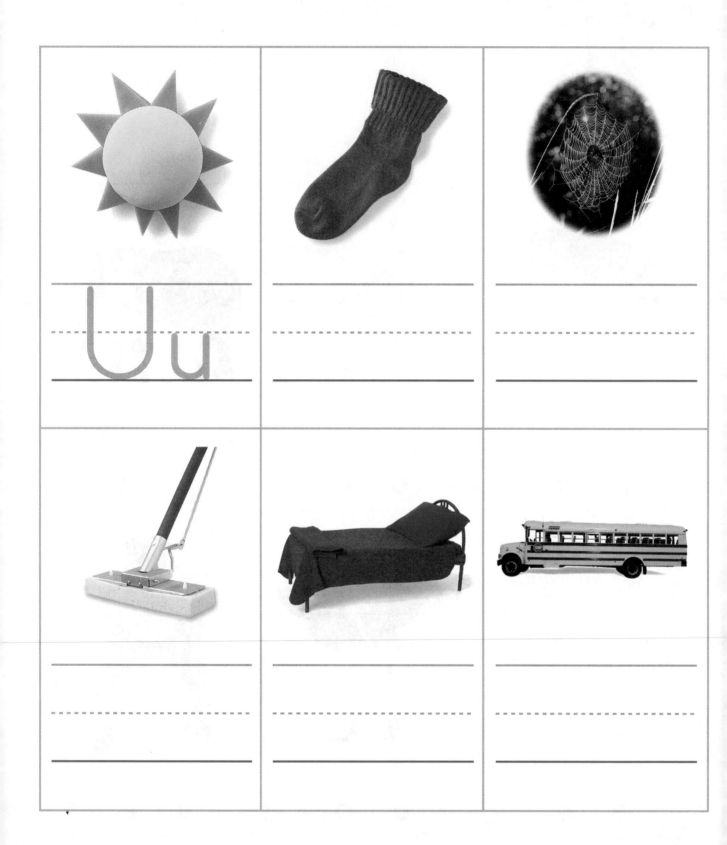

Directions: Have children say the name of each picture, listen for the short vowel sound in the middle of the word, and trace or write the letters *Uu*, *Oo*, or *Ee*.

Name ____________

Look at Me!

Do I look like a fox?

1

--- FOLD ---

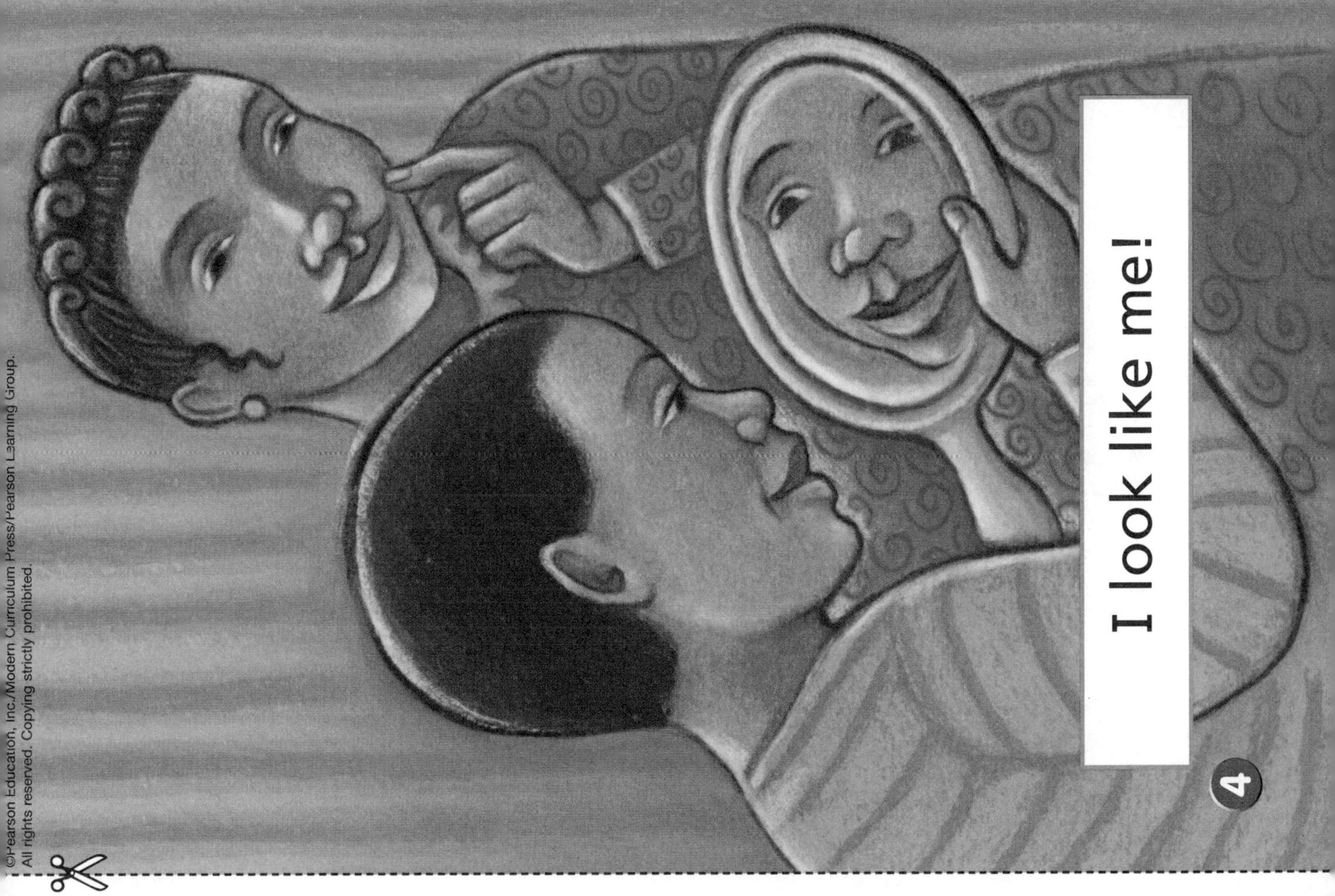

I look like me!

4

Directions: Read the story aloud and discuss the pictures with children.

2

Do I look like a bug?

FOLD

3

Do I look like a hen?

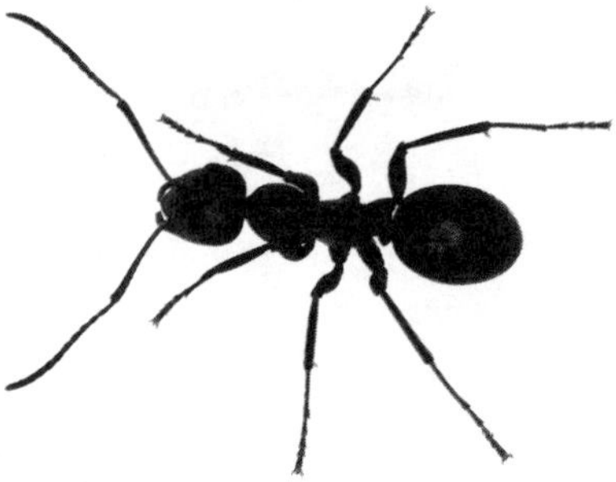 a i	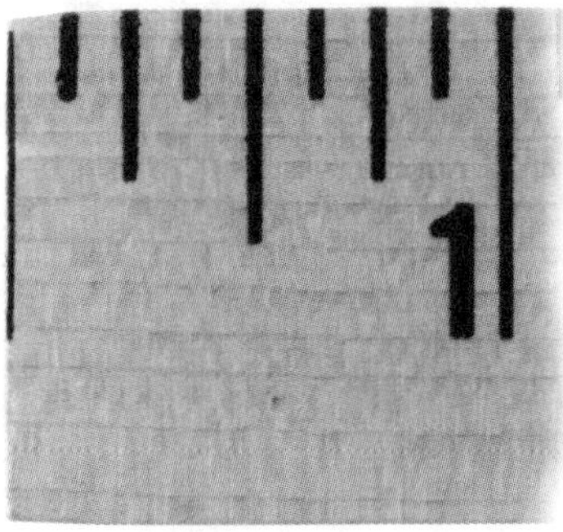 e i	 o u
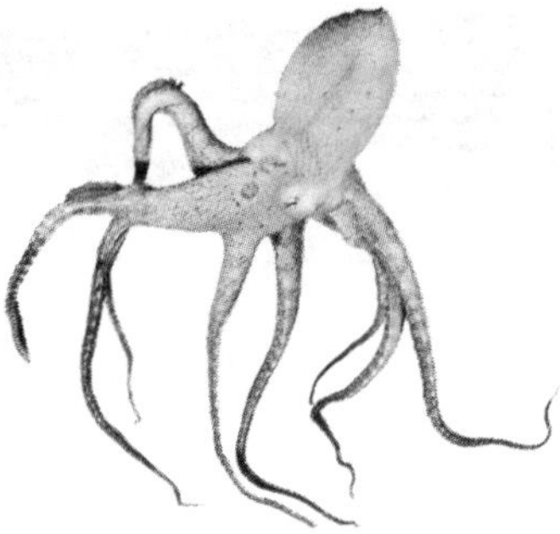 o a	 e u	 a i
 u a	 o i	 u e

Directions: Have children say the name of each picture, then circle the letter that stands for the beginning sound.

a i	e i	o u

o u	e a	u a

i e	a o	u o

Directions: Have children name the pictures, then trace the letter that stands for the middle vowel sound.

HOME Ask your child to name each picture, then say another word that rhymes.

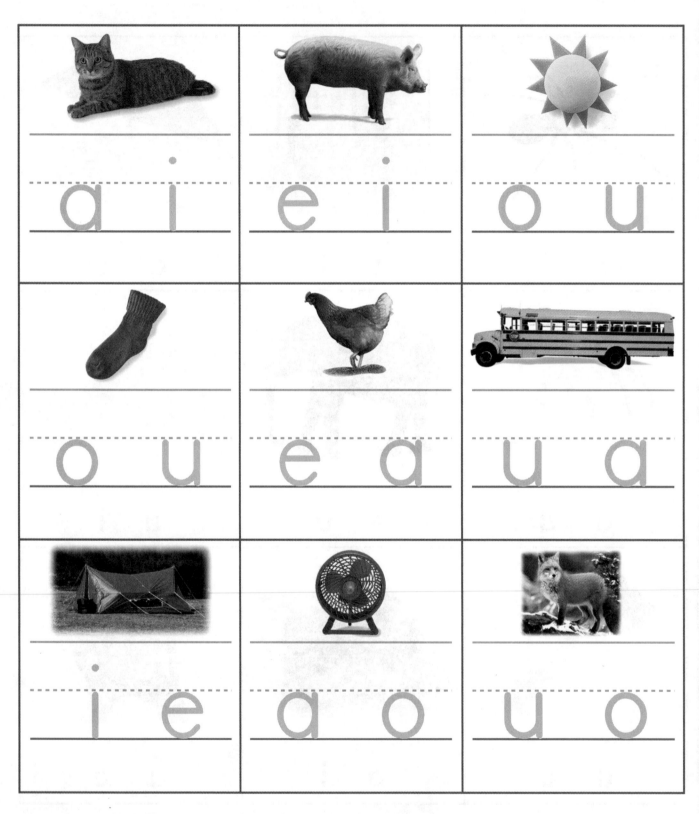

Read Aloud

The Picnic

by Dorothy Aldis

We brought a rug for sitting on.
Our lunch was in a box.
The sand was warm. We didn't wear
hats or shoes or socks.

Waves came curling up the beach.
We waded. It was fun.
Our sandwiches were different kinds,
I dropped my jelly one.

TALK About It What do you like to eat for lunch?

Dear Family,

In this unit "Fun in the Sun," your child will be introduced to the long vowel sounds of **a**, **e**, **i**, **o** and **u** in the middle of words. As your child developes an understanding of these sounds, you may wish to try these activities.

- Play a rhyming words game with your child by saying a word with a long vowel sound and having your child repeat the word and say a word that rhymes: cake-bake, meet-feet, bike-like, hole-mole, suit-fruit.
- Look through a toy catalog together to find and cut out pictures of items whose names have a long vowel sound, such as a bike, kite, skates, train, boat, jeep, game. Ask your child to say each picture name and think of another word that has the same middle vowel sound.
- Read aloud to your child. Look for stories about outdoor activities. Ask if these books are available in your local library.

Pretend You're a Cat
by Jean Marzollo

My Bunny and Me
by Lindsey Barrett George

Sincerely,

cube

skate

bike

Estimada familia:

En esta unidad, titulada "Diversión bajo el sol" ("Fun in the Sun"), su hijo/a estudiará los sonidos largos de las vocales **a**, **e**, **i**, **o** y **u** a la mitad de palabras en inglés. A medida que su hijo/a se vaya familiarizando con estos sonidos, pueden hacer las siguientes actividades juntos.

- Participen en un juego de rimas en el cual ustedes dicen una palabra con una vocal de sonido largo y su hijo/a debe repetir la palabra y decir otra que rime con ella: cake-bake, meet-feet, bike-like, hole-mole, suit-fruit.
- Hojeen juntos un catálogo de juguetes en busca de ilustraciones para recortar de artículos cuyos nombres tienen vocales de sonido largo, como bike, kite, skates, train, boat, jeep, game. Pidan a su hijo/a que diga el nombre de cada ilustración y piense en otra palabra que tenga a la mitad una vocal con el mismo sonido largo.
- Lean en voz alta a su hijo/a. Busquen cuentos sobre aventuras al aire libre. Pregunten en su biblioteca local si tienen disponibles estos libros.

Pretend You're a Cat
de Jean Marzollo

My Bunny and Me
de Lindsey Barrett George

Sinceramente,

Name ______________________________

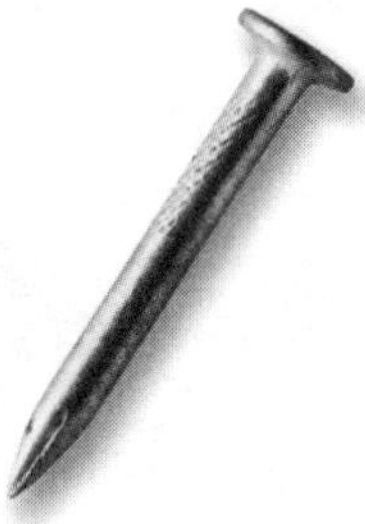

Directions: Help children say the names of the pictures in each row. Have them circle the pictures whose names rhyme.

Directions: Have children help the family get to the lake by coloring the pictures whose names have the long vowel *a* sound they hear in the middle of *lake*.

HOME

Ask your child to name each picture they colored and say another word that rhymes, such as *cape*, *base*, *page*, *name*.

Name ________________________________

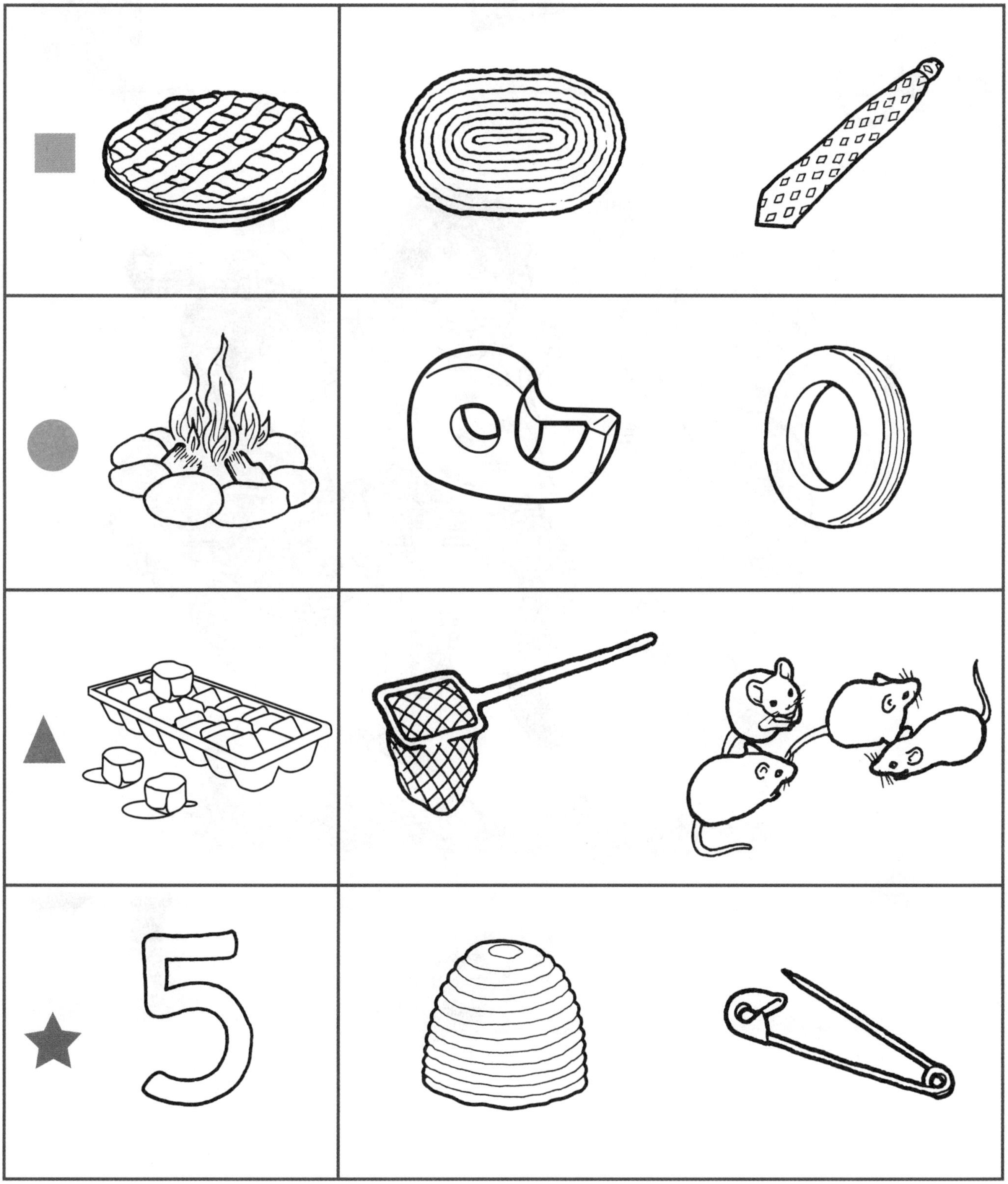

Directions: Help children say the names of the pictures in each row. Have them color the pictures whose names rhyme.

Directions: Invite children to name the pictures. Have them circle each picture whose name has the long vowel *i* sound as in *like*.

HOME Ask your child to name each picture they circled and say another word that rhymes, such as *hike*, *bite*, *mice*, *side*.

Name ______________________________

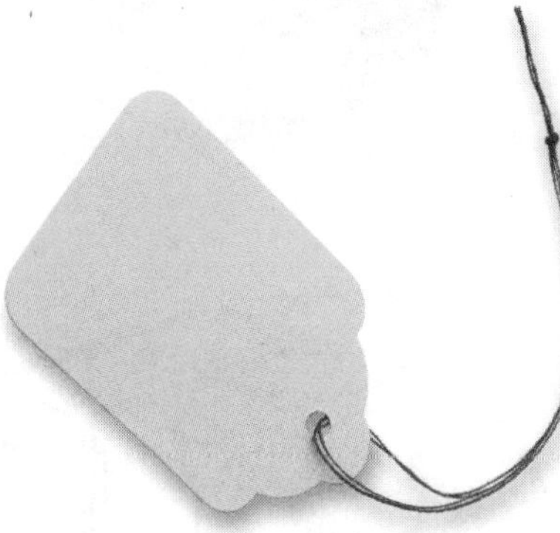

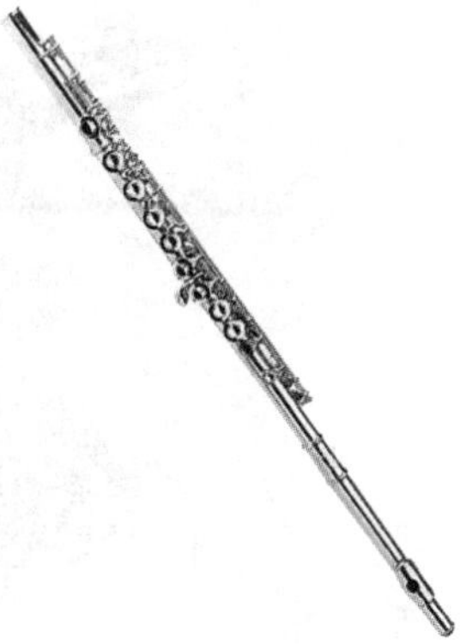

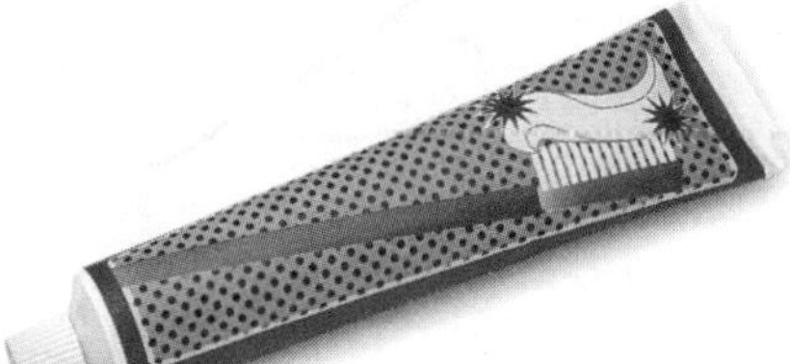

Directions: Help children say the names of the pictures in each row. Have them circle the pictures whose names have the same medial long vowel *u* sound.

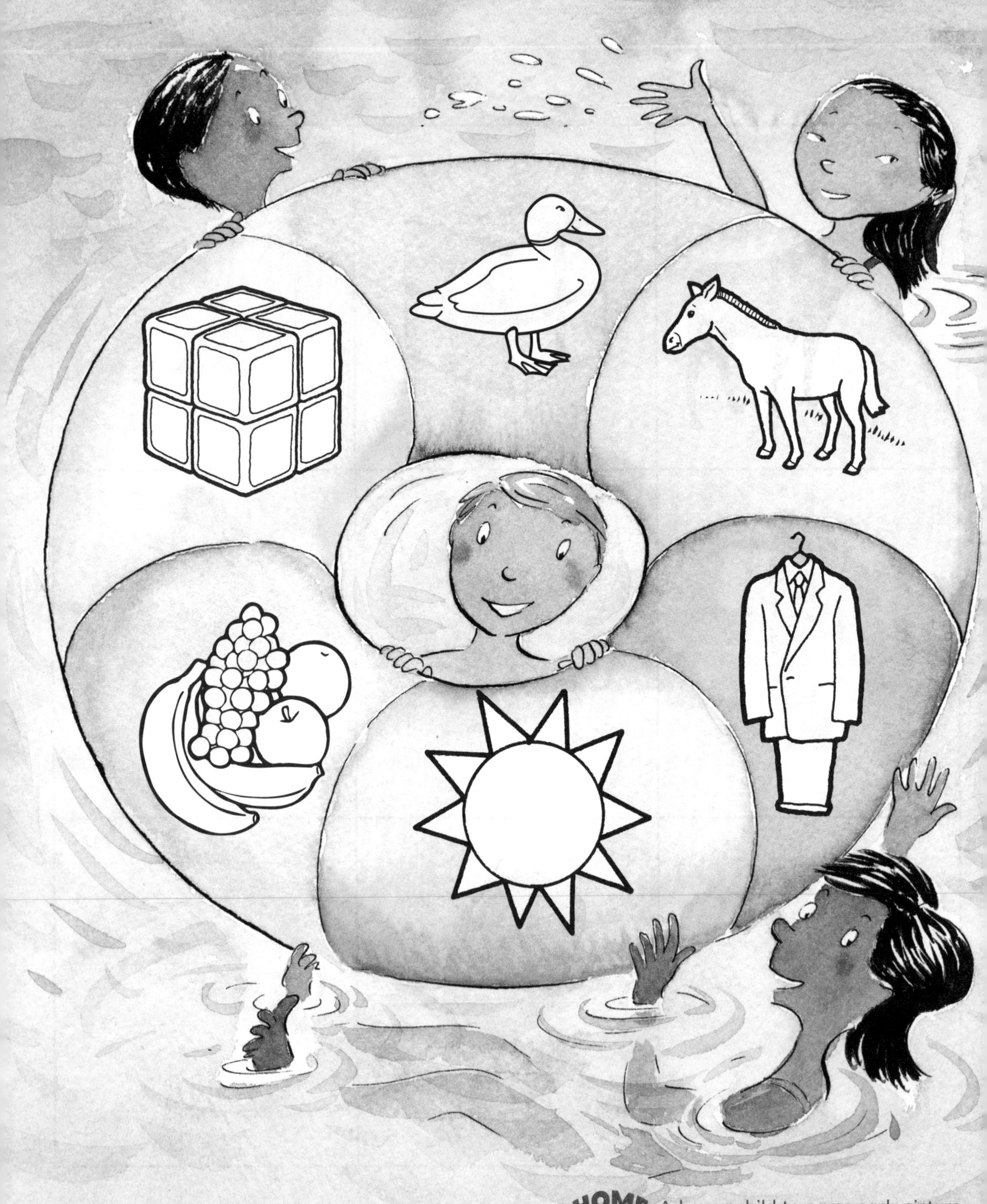

Directions: Help children name the pictures. Have them color each picture whose name has the long vowel *u* sound as in *tube*.

HOME

Ask your child to name each picture they colored and say another word that has the same long vowel *u* sound, such as *cute*, *flute*, *use*, *true*.

Name ______________________________

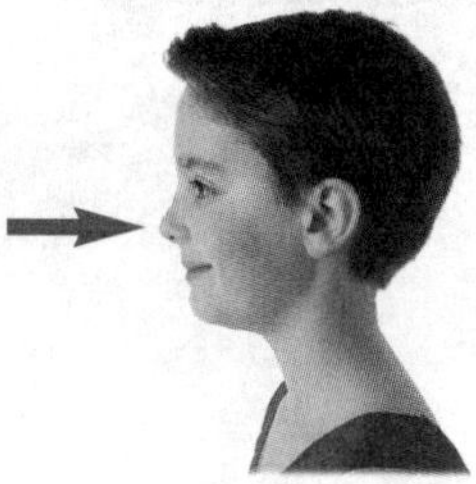

Directions: Help children say the names of the pictures in each column. Have them draw lines to match the pictures whose names rhyme.

Directions: Invite children to name the pictures. Have them help the family get to the dock by coloring each picture whose name has the long vowel *o* sound as in *boat*.

HOME Say the long o words *boat, bow, fold, so, coast*. Ask your child to say a word that rhymes.

Name ______________________________

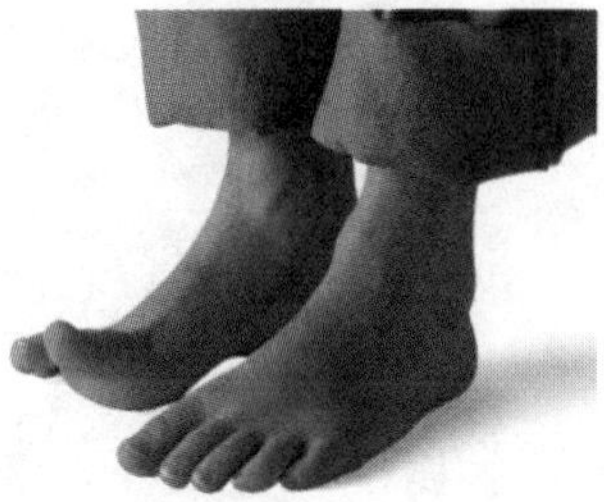

Directions: Help children say the names of the pictures in each column. Have them draw lines to match the pictures whose names rhyme.

Directions: Help children name the pictures on the shirts of the team members. Have them circle the pictures whose names have the sound of long vowel e as in *team*.

HOME Say the long e words *knee*, *sleep*, *neat*, *week*, *each*. Ask your child to say a word that rhymes.

Name ______________________________

	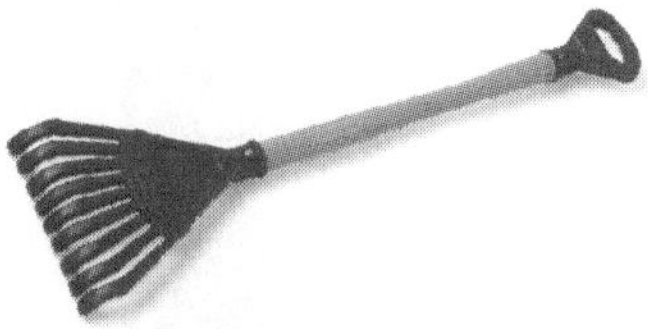	
	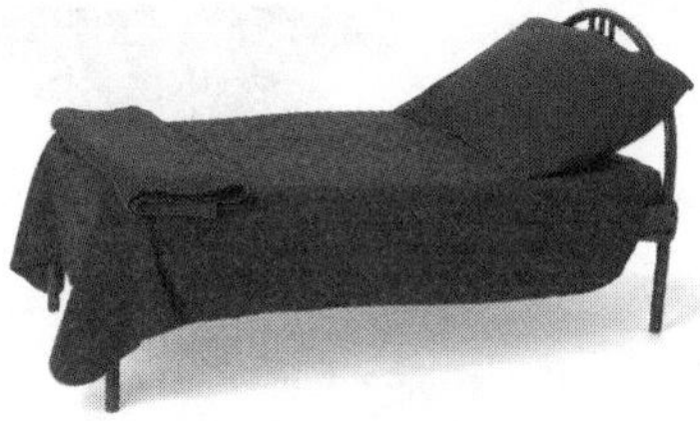	

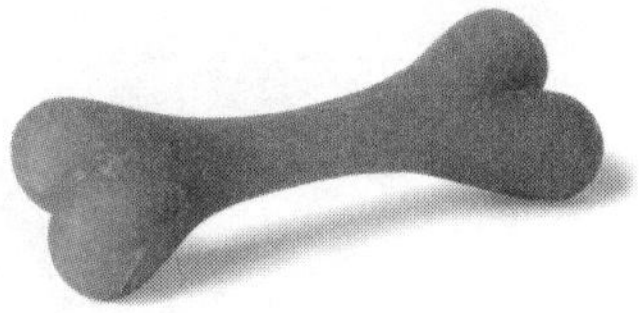		

Directions: Help children say the names of the pictures in each row. Have them circle the two pictures whose names rhyme.

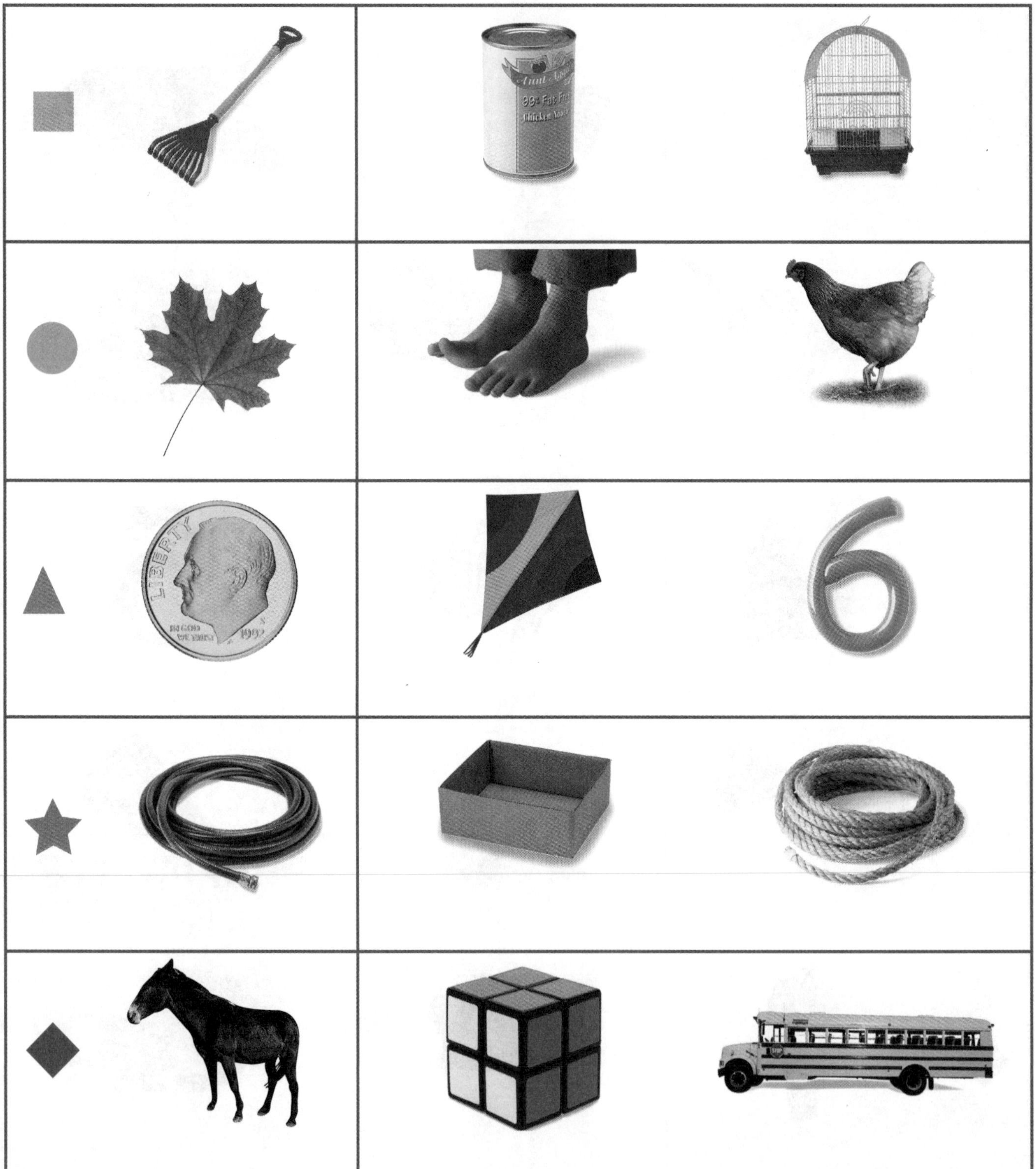

Directions: Help children to name the first picture in each row. Then, have them name the next two pictures and circle the one whose name has the same long vowel sound as the first picture.

HOME Ask your child to name the two pictures in each row with the same vowel sound, then say another word with the same vowel sound.

Name ______________________________

you **with**
are **can**

■ I can  with you.

● Can you  with me?

▲ You can  with me!

★ Now we are .

Directions: Read the words in the box and have children repeat them. Invite children to say and trace the word in each sentence. Then read the sentences with children.

You	with
are	can

■ You can .

● We are on the .

▲ You can not .

★ You can  with me.

Directions: Help children read each sentence, then have them trace each word to complete the sentence. Invite them to read each sentence again with you.

HOME Write the words from this lesson on a sheet of paper. Have your child say each word as you point to it.

Name ____________

At the Park

We can go to the park.

1

We take the bus home.

4

FOLD

We can ride the train.

2

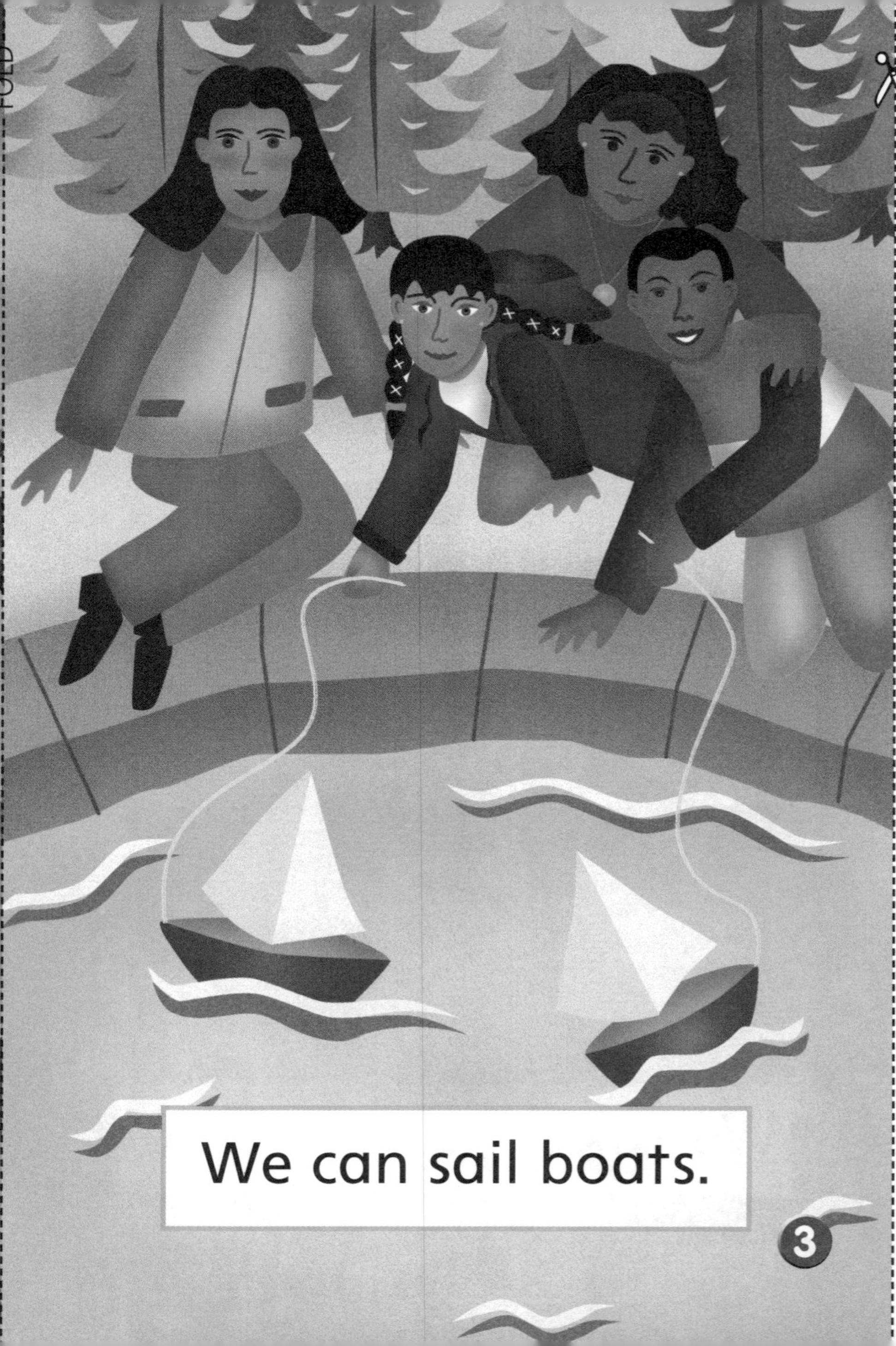

We can sail boats.

3

FOLD

UNIT 4 CHECKUP

Name ______________________________

Directions: Help children name the pictures in each column, then draw lines to match the pictures whose names rhyme.

Directions: Have children name the pictures in each row, then color the two pictures whose names have the same long vowel sound.

HOME Write the words from this lesson on a sheet of paper. Have your child say each word as you point to it.